ATOMIC EXPERIMENTS
FOR BOYS

OTHER BOOKS
BY THE SAME AUTHOR

A Boy and a Battery
A Boy and a Motor
The Boys' Book of Communications
The Boys' Book of Magnetism
The Boys' Book of Model Railroading
The Boys' Book of Rockets
Model Jets and Rockets for Boys

ATOMIC
EXPERIMENTS
FOR BOYS

by

Raymond
F. Yates

DRAWINGS
AND PHOTOGRAPHS
BY THE AUTHOR

HARPER & BROTHERS *Publishers* **NEW YORK**

CONTENTS

CHAPTER 1 *A Plus and Minus World* 1

CHAPTER 2 *Magnetism, Brother of Electricity* 17

CHAPTER 3 *Discovering the Electron* 26

CHAPTER 4 *Putting Atoms Together* 40

CHAPTER 5 *Energy, the Ghost of Matter* 50

CHAPTER 6 *Atomic Cousins: the Isotopes* 58

CHAPTER 7 *Watching Atomic Bullets and Explosions* 65

CHAPTER 8 *Miracle in a Pickle Jar* 72

CHAPTER 9 *Making Your Own Geiger Counter* 81

CHAPTER 10 *Simple Experiments with Radiation* 90

CHAPTER 11 *Atomic Merry-Go-Round* 98

CHAPTER 12 *How the Atomic Bomb Works* 108

CHAPTER 13 *The Atomic Pile* 115

CHAPTER 14 *Atomic Power* 123

CHAPTER 15 *The H-Bomb* 126

CHAPTER 16 *Prospecting for Uranium* 129

ACKNOWLEDGMENT

The author wishes to publicize his indebtedness to Mr. George L. Glaseen, chief of the Educational Services Section of the Atomic Energy Commission, Washington, D.C.

ILLUSTRATIONS

Fig. 1.   *Making electricity by friction.*   3

Fig. 2.   *Details of a simple homemade electroscope.*   4

Fig. 3.   *Discharging electroscopes by means of radio-
          active materials.*   8

Fig. 4.   *Demonstration of electrical attraction and
          repulsion.*   11

Fig. 5.   *Demonstration of the attraction and repulsion
          of static electrical charges.*   12

Fig. 6.   *Details of an improved electroscope.*   13

Fig. 7.   *Picture of the electroscope detailed in Fig. 6.*   15

Fig. 8.   *Demonstrating the existence of magnetic
          fields around a wire carrying electricity.*   19

Fig. 9.   *Demonstrating attraction and repulsion with
          two steel bar magnets.*   21

Fig. 10. *Proving that a wire carrying electricity acts
          as a magnet.*   22

Fig. 11. *Demonstrating the relationship between mag-
          netism and electricity.*   23

Fig. 12. *Showing how an electrically charged coil will
          act as a magnet.*   24

Fig. 13. *Demonstrating the passage of electricity
          through an evacuated glass tube.*   28

Fig. 14. *Operating a modern Geissler tube.* 29

Fig. 15. *Showing how electrons passing through an evacuated glass tube are pulled from their paths by a magnet.* 31

Fig. 16. *Demonstrating how electrically charged particles cast a shadow in an evacuated glass tube.* 32

Fig. 17. *Diverting electrified particles in an evacuated glass tube with a charged metal plate.* 34

Fig. 18. *Showing that high voltage electrons will pass through thin aluminum foil.* 37

Fig. 19. *Diagrammatic representations of the electron, proton, and neutron.* 41

Fig. 20. *How the electrons swirl about the core or nucleus of an atom.* 42

Fig. 21. *How the neutrons and protons are packed together in the nucleus of atoms.* 44

Fig. 22. *Diagram showing the principle of the chain reaction.* 45

Fig. 23. *Diagrammatic representation of the atom of Uranium 238.* 47

Fig. 24. *The arrangements of the atom of hydrogen and its two isotopes H_2 and H_3; and the atomic arrangements of Carbon 12, 13, and 14.* 61

Fig. 25. *Diagram of a simple homemade spinthariscope.* 66

Fig. 26. *Picture of spinthariscope detailed in Fig. 25.* 67

Fig. 27. *Construction details of a Wilson cloud chamber.*   75

Fig. 28. *The complete Wilson cloud chamber in a glass jar.*   76

Fig. 29. *Setting up the Wilson cloud chamber for use.*   77

Fig. 30. *How particles and rays appear in the Wilson cloud chamber.*   79

Fig. 31. *Simple principle of the Geiger counter.*   84

Fig. 32. *A simple Geiger counter and the parts for making it.*   87

Fig. 33. *Shadow photograph made by the author.*   93

Fig. 34. *Arrangement of the D's between the powerful magnets of a cyclotron.*   99

Fig. 35. *Small cyclotron at the University of Rochester.* 102

Fig. 36. *How the explosion of one atom is communicated to adjacent atoms.*   113

Fig. 37. *A simple atomic pile.*   118

Fig. 38. *A great nuclear reactor or uranium pile.*   122

Fig. 39. *Converting atomic energy into a usable form.*   124

CHAPTER 1

A Plus and Minus World

WE LIVE IN A GREAT SEA OF ELECTRICITY, some of it in motion, some of it standing still. When electricity is in motion as through wires, coils, telephones or electric lights, it is called "current electricity." When it is standing still it is called "static electricity" and the body upon which it is resting is said to be "charged."

In any event, electricity is made up of swarms of the smallest particle in the universe, the electron, which we might say is itself a purely electrical particle. Some of these busy (or lazy!) particles are among those that make up the atoms of matter and are therefore forever captive. It is the roving electrons, the free ones, that provide us with the electric current that has become such a great and useful servant of mankind. Countless billions of such particles must pass through a motor or an electric light each second of time to keep it operating. When

1

electrons move rapidly through wires, the voltage is said to be high. The larger the number of them passing a given point each second, the greater the amperage of the current formed by them. The electron itself is a negative particle of electricity.

If we are to understand atoms and atomic energy, we will have to investigate this business of electrical charges in our home laboratory. Fortunately many interesting and instructive experiments may be conducted with instruments that can be made in a jiffy.

Before we start construction of our instruments, however, let us conduct a few experiments with static electricity which we can easily generate ourselves. As our first adventure, let us cut up some small pieces of dry paper about one half the size of postage stamps. We then rub a vinyl phonograph record briskly either with a piece of dry silk or woolen cloth. After this, the record is brought near the bits of paper. Lo and behold, the paper bits are drawn to the record and remain fixed to its surface as though held with an adhesive.

For another experiment, (see Fig. 1) we place a dry, clean piece of glass over the paper which is in turn placed in the top of a tin coffee can. After the surface of the glass is rubbed briskly with either the piece of woolen or silken cloth, the paper bits will fly upward and fix themselves to the bottom of the glass in defiance of gravity.

A simple device that can be assembled on a kitchen

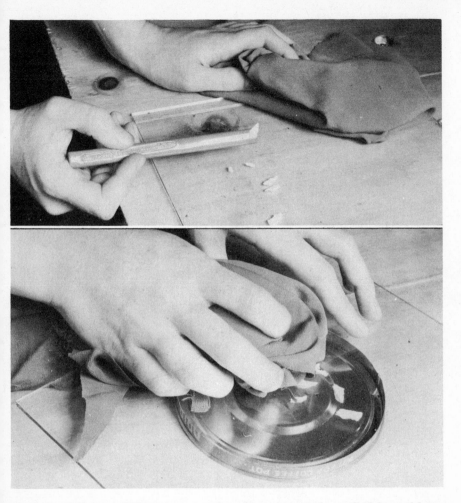

FIG. 1.   (Above) When a piece of sealing wax is electrified by rubbing it with dry woolen or silk cloth, it will attract small bits of paper. (Below) A few bits of paper are placed in an inverted coffee can top and a piece of glass is placed over this. When the glass is rubbed briskly with a piece of silk cloth, the glass will become electrified and attract the bits of paper, lifting them upward.

table will detect the presence of electrical charges. This
is called an electroscope and it is contained in a peanut-
butter jar. The drawing (Fig. 2) will supply full details
of construction. It is most important that the piece of
wire carrying the two thin leaves of metal foil be perfectly insulated (electrically) from the metal top of the
peanut-butter jar at the point where it passes through.
This is done either with molten sulphur or sealing wax.

Although gold leaf such as used for signs on store win-

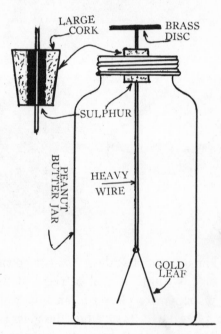

FIG. 2.   Details for a simple homemade electroscope with
which many experiments in electrification may be carried out.

dows is very fine for use as the metal leaves on electroscopes, it is difficult to handle unless we take our instrument to a sign painter and have him put the gold leaf in place.

A substitute metal leaf much heavier and therefore less sensitive than the gold may be had from the metal foil now used to wrap chewing gum. If a piece of such a wrapper is soaked in rubbing alcohol for a few moments, it will be found that the metal foil may be separated from the paper and placed over the end of the wire in the manner illustrated.

Before the electroscope is assembled for final use, it should be heated gently to make sure that all moisture is driven from all of its surfaces. Otherwise, our experiments will fail. Even a damp, humid day may make them far less exciting.

To charge the electroscope, we pass a dry comb through our hair several times and then bring the comb near the top of the electroscope. Instantly the leaves inside the electroscope will fly apart and remain that way showing that they have received an electric charge. If left alone the leaves will gradually come back together again, the time required depending upon the conditions of the surrounding air, etc. In the case of professional electroscopes, this charge might be maintained for hours.

Under certain conditions that we may easily bring about, the metal leaves within the jar can be made to lose their electrical charge and come back together very quickly. For one thing, all we need to do is to bring the flame of a lighted candle within an inch or so of the top of the electroscope when the leaves will come together quickly.

If the electroscope is placed in the vicinity of x-rays or a piece of radioactive material, its charge will also be quickly lost. The speed with which the leaves come together will be a direct index of the power of either the x-rays or the radioactive material. If, for instance, the leaves of an electroscope would collapse quickly even though radioactive material is a long way off, it is known that a dangerous quantity of radioactivity is near. The electroscope, as a result, finds many uses in atomic research and in the manufacture of atomic materials.

What really happens in the case of the candle, the x-rays and the radioactive material is that each one of these things permit the air around the top of the electroscope to conduct electricity. Therefore the electrical charges carried by the leaves within the electroscope have a chance to escape.

Some of our most interesting experiments with mildly radioactive materials can be conducted with this electroscope or better still, with the more professional type instrument described at the end of this Chapter. We will find, for instance, that radiation (particles and rays) given off radioactive substances have the power to pass through various materials. This power will depend upon the intensity or power of the radiation, its type, and the nature and thickness of the material through which it passes.

The experiment shown in Fig. 3 will demonstrate these things. Here, the electroscope is first charged and then the radioactive material or the lighted candle is placed nearby with a barrier placed between it and the electroscope. In the case of the candle, the discharging effect is easily screened off even with a piece of cardboard because heat is the active agent. In the case of radioactive material, however, it will be found that the cardboard will have little effect, the rays or particles coming from the radioactive material pass through cardboard very easily. A piece of glass will stop them more effectively but not entirely. A sheet of lead, however, will screen them off entirely unless we have such a powerful agent as to be dangerous.

No young scientist can understand the modern theory of matter or atomic energy without knowing something about electrical charge. This is the "glue" that holds matter together. We have perhaps heard the terms "negative" and "positive" but what do they mean? The student who would grasp the fundamentals of atomic energy would do well to confine his attention to the matter of electric charges.

At the base of all electric or electronic phenomena is

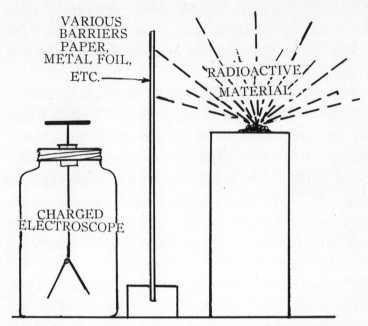

FIG. 3. Charged electroscopes may be discharged by rendering the air about them conductive. Radioactive material will do this. The speed with which the radiation from the radioactive material will discharge the electroscope will depend upon the power of the radioactivity and upon the nature of the screen shown between the electroscope and the radioactive material. Thin paper will do very little, while lead foil will impose a great barrier.

the fact that we have one of three electric conditions associated with matter. It makes little difference where we are; in the jungles, in the air, under the surface of the earth, in heat or in cold; the things around us are either electrically neutral or they bear what is known as a positive or a negative charge.

Some of these charges are so slight as to make it impossible to detect them, even with the most sensitive instruments. Other charges, such as those in the higher atmosphere, accumulate to such a degree that discharges two or three miles long take place, quite suddenly and explosively. We call these discharges "lightning."

If our eyes were sensitive to electric effects, we would be able to see many interesting and unsuspected things. Most things with which we deal are constantly in a more or less electrically agitated condition; that is, they are either positively or negatively charged. We cannot strike a match, cut a piece of paper, polish furniture, walk on a carpet or even breathe without in some small way affecting the electrical charges distributed throughout our immediate environment. The electricity in the world is in a constantly changing state, leaving one place and accumulating in another.

The things about us and beyond us, indeed all things, are either neutral electrically or they are positive or negative. Barring atomic particles, they are not, however, positive, negative or neutral in a lasting sense. That which is neutral this instant may be electrically positive or negative in the next instant and a body carrying a positive charge may, under the proper conditions, be changed to negative in the ten-thousandth part of a second. There is rarely any permanency to such conditions and oftentimes the most elaborate precautions have to be taken to electrically isolate a charged body in such a way as to preserve its charge.

The behavior of these charges, positive and negative, toward each other is important, for upon this behavior rests a great deal of our electrical and atomic theory. Fortunately, this behavior is relatively simple and the action of electric charges under precise conditions is always predictable. When two negatively charged bodies are brought into close relationship, they *repel* each other. The same holds for positively charged bodies. Hence, we may set it down as an unchangeable rule that *like charges of electricity repel each other*. Not so with *unlike* charges. These *attract* each other. Unless we firmly anchor these two facts in thought NOW, we might just as well abandon all further thought of studying atoms, for many of the things that we shall be trying to learn will be unintelligible without these basic concepts.

Still further proof of the nature and behavior of electrical charges can be gained from the simple home experiment shown in Fig. 4. Here two gilded ping-pong balls are suspended from fine wire. Normally, these balls will be electrically neutral and will therefore remain at rest in contact each with the other. If they are both charged either negatively or positively, they will fly apart.

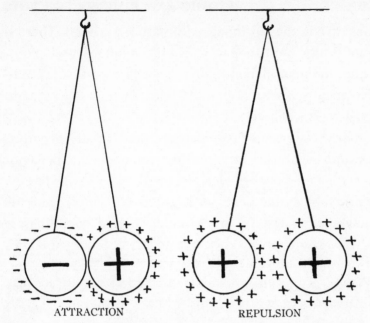

ATTRACTION   REPULSION

FIG. 4. Gilded ping-pong balls suspended with fine wires
will demonstrate both electrical attraction and repulsion.
They are electrified in the manner described in the text.

If one is charged positively and the other negatively, they
will be strongly attracted to each other.

The reason for the leaves of the electroscope flying
apart under the influence of electric charge is not difficult
to understand. Here we have a thin sheet of metal bearing one charge (which may be either + or −) folded
on itself. Hence both ends will be in contact and, being
free to move, will fly apart when the metal foil receives
an electric charge.

A more professional type of electroscope is shown in

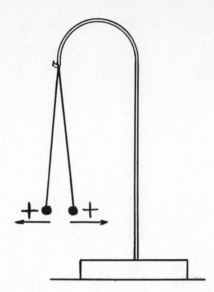

FIG. 5. Two pith balls suspended by fine silk threads may be used to demonstrate the attraction and repulsion of static charges of electricity.

Fig. 6. Although very simply built from very simple and inexpensive materials, this instrument will permit us to measure the rate at which the leaves of the instrument come together and, as we will later see, this will give us some idea of the power of the radioactivity of the materials being tested.

The dimensions of this electroscope are not important and practically all of the construction details may be gathered from the drawing. The case can be made from dry plywood shellacked to prevent undue accumulation of moisture. It is put together by the use of small brads.

As will be noted by the drawing, a thin strip of gold

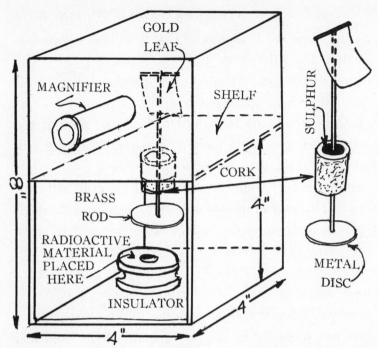

FIG. 6. Details of an improved electroscope that can be employed in experiments relating to radiation and atomic energy.

leaf is mounted near the top of the small brass rod which carries a small, polished brass disc soldered to its lower end. It is best that we take this assembly to a local sign painter and have him attach the piece of gold leaf to the rod by means of a touch of shellac. The box should be taken along, too, that the gold leaf may be protected by actually mounting it in the box after it has been attached to the rod.

It will be noticed that the rod passes through a cork

bushing filled with sulphur so that it will be completely insulated from the wood through which it passes. The sulphur can be gently heated until it melts after which it is poured into the space between the cord and the brass rod. Care should be taken not to heat the sulphur too much while it is being melted. Too much heating will destroy its insulating properties.

To detect very slight movements of the gold leaf as it loses its charge and drops back to the brass rod to which it is attached, we equip our electroscope with a small magnifying glass mounted in a brass or metal tube and so arranged that the tube may be moved in and out for proper focusing.

For purposes of comparison, we will need a scale of some sort mounted in the background of the gold leaf and against which it may be viewed. A combination scale and window is made by drawing the scale (with India ink) on a small piece of clear glass mounted over an opening in the rear of the instrument.

A glass window is also made to cover the chamber (called ionization chamber) opening in the lower part of the instrument case. It is here that the samples of radioactive material are placed, after the electroscope has been charged. The rays coming from such material will render the air in the chamber conductive which will permit the electric charge on the gold leaf to leak away. The speed of this leakage will depend upon the degree

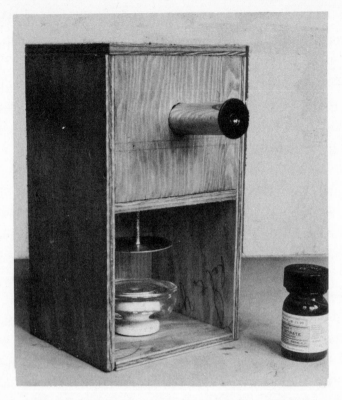

FIG. 7. The electroscope detailed in Fig. 6.

of radioactivity of the specimen,* which is mounted on an insulator placed directly beneath the brass disc at the end of the brass rod. A powerful, concentrated pinch of radium bromide would cause the leaf to drop immediately. Weak samples of radioactive materials might permit the gold leaf to maintain its charge for a half hour or more.

* Samples of carnotite, a radioactive ore, may be had from most chemical supplies houses.

All electrical charges, no matter how powerful they may be or where they may accumulate, are due to the *absence* or to the *presence* of a sub-atomic unit found as a constituent of all atoms. This smallest of all particles is called an electron and really it amounts to a negative unit of electricity.

But while such electrons are units of all atoms of matter, countless trillions of them lead a sort of wandering life, orphans we call them. When some of this free horde accumulate on a body, that body becomes negatively charged. When they leave it, the body may become positively charged. More wonderful still when such electrons are crowded together and herded through electric wires, they become electric current or, as we say, electricity. The larger the number of them passing through a wire the greater the *amperage* of the current or its capacity to do work. The greater the speed of the passing electrons, the greater the *voltage* of the electric current. Sometimes the speed of electrons reach such great heights that they will leap across open space and cause a spark. Then again they can be herded in such great numbers at low voltage (speed) that they may be made to melt metals together as in the case of welding.

However, before we learn more about the electron and how it was discovered, let us discover for ourselves the strange relationship between electricity and magnetism.

CHAPTER 2

Magnetism, Brother
of Electricity

WHATEVER THE REAL NATURE OF ELECTRIC charges, we know that they are utterly invisible and that some sort of mysterious action takes place in the space that separates charged bodies in the act of repelling or attracting each other. The same holds true of magnetism. Here, too, we discover the power of this invisible force to repel or attract through space. There is also a strange and mysterious relationship between electrical charges and magnetism; indeed between electricity (either current or static) and magnetism. Magnetism is also a mysterious part of the "glue" that holds matter together and that plays such an important part in the production and control of radioactive materials.

If we have thought of magnetism at all during the past,

we have probably thought of it only in connection with attraction. Few boys have grown to manhood without at some time or other having been mystified by a small horseshoe magnet and its curious power to pull nails to it and lift relatively heavy pieces of iron or steel.

Perhaps most of our education with magnetism began and ended with such simple experiments. However, that is only a part of the fascinating story. Magnetism is something more than a strange property of iron or steel. Whenever an electric current (either a.c. or d.c.) passes through an electric wire, a magnetic influence (called a field) is set up around such a wire and spreads out with the wire as a center but becoming weaker and weaker (see Fig. 8) as the distance from the wire is increased. This so-called "field," as in the case of the electrified bodies described in the previous Chapter, involves mysterious, invisible fingers that reach out from a magnetized body and either *pull* or *push* on a nearby body. In the case of an ordinary horseshoe or bar steel magnet, these invisible fingers (lines of force, they are called by scientists) are referred to as a magnetic field. However, the magnetism or magnetic field found about a wire carrying an electric current is referred to as an electromagnetic field meaning, as we might easily guess, that the magnetism has been created by the passage of an electric current.

A few very simple experiments with bar magnets will

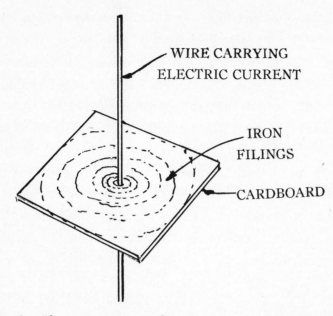

WIRE CARRYING
ELECTRIC CURRENT

IRON
FILINGS

CARDBOARD

FIG. 8. If a wire carrying electric current passes through a paper upon which some fine iron filings have been sprinkled, the tiny particles of iron will tend to arrange themselves in circles as illustrated. These circles show the shape of the invisible magnetic field around such a wire.

prove to us that a certain peculiar relationship exists between magnetism and electricity. Indeed in so far as ordinary, everyday use of electricity is concerned, one is impossible without the other.

The similarity that strikes us is the fact that, like charges of electricity, magnetism can both attract (pull) and repel (push). Most of us have thought that magnets have only the power to attract.

In the case of bodies carrying an electric charge, this may be either positive or negative. Magnets, on the other hand, no matter what form they assume, have a *north* and a *south* pole. These terms have no geographical meaning except that the earth itself behaves in the manner of a great magnet and that it has a South and a North pole.

When the north pole of a magnet is brought near the south pole of another magnet, the one will attract the other with considerable force; enough force indeed to defy gravity (See Fig. 9). However, when one magnet is turned around and the north and south poles of each are arranged opposite each other, the forces of repulsion or "pushing away" will come into play. In the case of powerful magnets, this "pushing away" may become so violent as actually to toss the one free magnet into the air.

If we have an ordinary pocket compass and a dry cell about, we can very easily demonstrate this strange and mysterious relationship between electricity and magnetism. In the case of bringing the wires together as in Fig. 10, electric current will flow from the dry cell, and when the contact is made and current flows, the little needle of the compass will swing violently. In this case, the electricity flowing through the wire creates magnetism around the wire. Thus we put it down that electricity

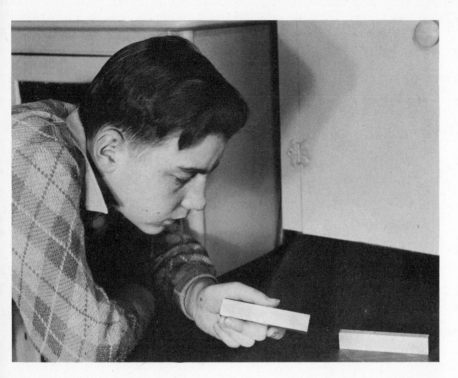

FIG. 9. Demonstrating with two steel bar magnets. When two north poles of such magnets are brought together, the magnets will repel or push each other away. When the north pole of one magnet is brought near the south pole of another magnet, the magnets will attract each other.

can create magnetism. Can the reverse be true; can magnetism create electricity?

If we turn to Fig. 11 we will note that magnetism can indeed create electricity. If we make a small coil of wire and loop one turn of it out for a few feet, we will set the stage for the experiment. We move the loop out so that

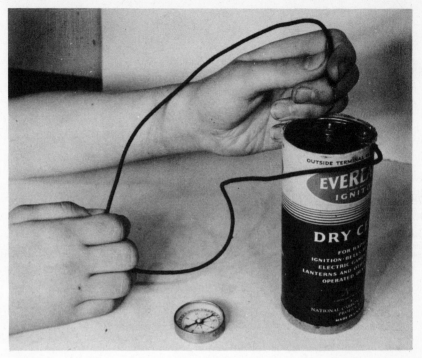

Fig. 10. That a wire carrying electricity acts as a magnet can be proven by this experiment. When current flows in the wire, the compass needle will be agitated.

the compass will be too far away to be affected by the magnet itself. After the long loop is made, the raw ends of the wire comprising the coil and the loop are connected together. The pocket compass is placed near the end of the wire loop as close to the wire as possible.

We now take a bar or horseshoe magnet and move it in the vicinity of the coil of wire keeping our eye on the needle of the compass in the meantime. We note that

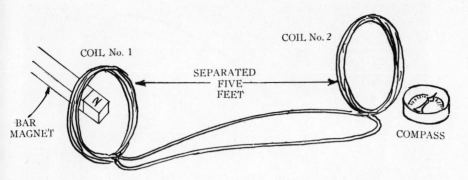

COIL No. 1

COIL No. 2

SEPARATED
FIVE
FEET

BAR
MAGNET

COMPASS

FIG. 11. This experiment demonstrates the relationship between magnetism and electricity. When the magnet is moved within Coil No. 1, the compass needle near Coil No. 2 will be agitated, showing that electricity is generated in both coils. When the magnet is motionless, no electricity will flow.

every time we move the magnet the needle of the compass will give a slight jerk proving that a current of electricity is flowing through the distant wire of the coil. This happens only when the magnet is moved. When it is held motionless over the coil no current is generated. This, incidentally is the principle used for the generation of electricity by means of the dynamo.

Now we have proven by means of very simple experiments that electricity will generate magnetism and that, in turn, magnetism will generate electricity. There appears to be a brother-and-sister relationship between the two.

We have stated before that electricity, whether standing still (static) or moving (current) is caused by elec-

Fɪɢ. 12. When current from the battery flows through the suspended coil, the coil will act like a magnet, being either attracted or repelled by the steel magnet depending upon the pole of the steel magnet brought nearest the coil.

trons. In the case of electric current, these electrons go streaming through wires at high speed. In the case of charged bodies, they simply accumulate and remain motionless.

A magnet as in Fig. 11 can be used as a sort of "pump" to start the flow of electrons in wires and once a flow of electrons is started, they in turn generate magnetism which forms a field around the wire. The strength of this magnetism about the wire will depend upon the number of electrons flowing each second of time.

Electrons that remain motionless on charged bodies do not produce such magnetic fields.

CHAPTER 3

Discovering the Electron

ALTHOUGH MANY MEN OF SCIENCE HAD thought prior to 1880 that matter was somehow or other closely related to electricity, they could produce no experimental evidence to support their views. It was about this time that Sir William Crookes and Professor J. J. Thomson appeared. Their work and their names will go thundering down through the centuries to come. Through their efforts and to a lesser degree the efforts of other men, the basis of the electron theory was set down.

Prior to the appearance of these two experimenters, what was known as the atomic theory of matter held and was generally accepted. The chemistry books of that day stated that matter was composed entirely of atoms and that these were the smallest particles known to man. Really this was nothing but a good guess. No one could see an atom. Atoms were far too small for that. Some eighty-odd elements of matter were known at the time and each element was supposed to have its own atom. There were the atoms of lead, copper, oxygen, etc. Some atoms were heavier than others, and some were more active (chemically, that is) than others. The elements themselves were the basic things of creation. By this was meant that the universe and all that was in it was composed of these elements alone and in combinations with other elements to form what was known as compounds. For instance, when the element hydrogen combined with the element oxygen, the compound water (H_2O) was formed and the resulting union of atoms was called a molecule. The molecule of water was particularly simple. Others involved the union of more atoms and were far more complicated. In a nutshell, this was the status of our ideas about matter and chemistry prior to the appearance of that smallest of all things, the mighty electron.

Of course, the inquiring minds of those pre-electron days were constantly wondering what atoms really were and if they were composed of still smaller particles.

Geissler, a relatively unknown physicist, back as far as 1860, lighted up one of the dark corners of physics and supplied Sir William Crookes with many of his ideas when he (Geissler) evacuated a small glass tube (that is, he pumped out as much air as he could) and sealed two electrodes (metal conductors) in the tube. He was trying to find out how electric current might behave when confronted with a vacuum. Could it leap across? Geissler found (see Fig. 13) that under ordinary circumstances, it could not. However, as he raised the voltage of the electric current (and by voltage we mean the moving or "pushing power" of the current), he finally reached a point where the jump between the electrodes was made. Curiously enough when the electricity jumped the gap, it caused the tube to light up, giving off a weird blue color. It was all very strange and indeed very confusing.

It was not long after Geissler's work that Sir William Crookes set about evacuating glass tubes and sending electricity through them. He thought a great deal about the strange, weird light coming from these tubes. Many of the experimenters of the day who heard of Crookes' work were quick with an explanation. They believed that

FIG. 13. Geissler, a German experimenter, discovered that electricity will pass through an evacuated glass tube when the voltage is high enough. When this is done, such tubes will give off a soft bluish-green light. (From *The Working Electron* by Raymond F. Yates. Harper & Brothers, New York. 1946.)

atoms of matter (in the electrodes, no doubt) were simply torn away by the action of the electricity and hurled across the space between the electric conductors or electrodes sealed in the ends of the glass tube. The light?

Fɪɢ. 14. Operating a modern Geissler tube by connecting it to a high-voltage sparking or induction coil. Geissler tubes are inexpensive and may be operated from old Ford ignition coils.

Oh, that was merely due to collisions taking place between the flying atoms and the few atoms of the atmospheric gases remaining in the tube.

Crookes was not so sure. He thought that such an explanation amounted to oversimplification. For a long time, he was much inclined toward the view that there was a "fourth state of matter," and that the particles, *if* they were particles, represented this fourth state or "radiant matter." Matter was at that time, and still is, considered to be in three basic forms; solids, liquids, and gases. Sir William thought that his state of "radiant matter" was as far removed from a gas as gases are from liquids. In short, he visualized a very "fine" state of matter.

Crookes next performed one of the greatest classical experiments of all time. Before we explain this, let us for a moment examine the Crookes' tube in Fig. 15. We note the sealed-in metal electrodes. We have learned that the residual or "left-in" atmospheric gases in the tube were caused to become luminous when bombarded with the flying particles, whatever they might be. But the gases were not the only things that became luminous or "fluorescent." Apparently, some of the swiftly moving particles flew on to the end of the glass tube and struck it. The glass itself then glowed in a peculiar fashion, giving off a kind of light.

Would shadows be cast in this light as in ordinary

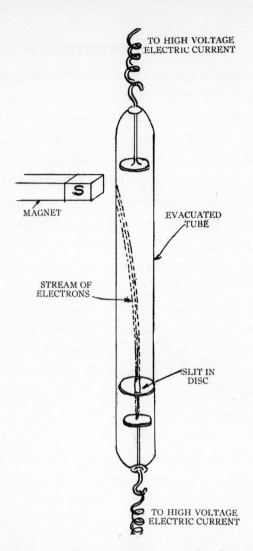

TO HIGH VOLTAGE
ELECTRIC CURRENT

MAGNET

EVACUATED
TUBE

STREAM OF
ELECTRONS

SLIT IN
DISC

TO HIGH VOLTAGE
ELECTRIC CURRENT

FIG. 15. Early experiments with electrical discharges through evacuated glass tubes showed that the streams of electrons set in motion within such tubes could be pulled out of their normal paths by a magnet.

light? That was a question that Sir William asked himself, and he answered it by the aid of a simple but ingenious device shown in Fig. 16. He mounted one metal
electrode so it would cast a shadow. The result was a
definite shadow cast on the end of the tube. Still, no
definite answer could be given as to the nature of the
particles, nor could it really be said that the phenomenon
was caused by particles. Perhaps a new form of light was
being generated.

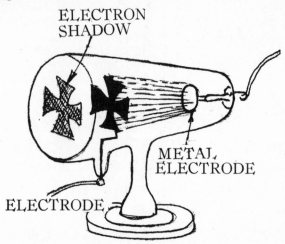

ELECTRON
SHADOW

METAL
ELECTRODE

ELECTRODE

Fig. 16.   Sir William Crookes, the English scientist, experi-
mented with many types of evacuated glass tubes through
which he passed high-voltage electricity. In one of these
(shown above) he showed that the particles within the tube
that were set in motion would cast a shadow at the end of
the tube. Crookes did not know at the time that these particles were electrons.

Subsequent experiments, however, showed pretty conclusively that particles they were, and that they were moving at ultra-high speed, perhaps as fast as 20,000 miles per second.

Naturally the experimenters of the time, principally Professor J. J. Thomson, were anxious to find out whether or not the particles (if they were particles) had any electrical properties. If they were particles, perhaps they bore an electric charge, either positive or negative. A good way to find out would be to use the simple arrangement illustrated in Fig. 17, a special kind of tube set up with a sealed-in metal electrode which would not be connected in any way to the metal electrodes or terminals carrying the high-voltage electricity into the tube, and with a third conductor placed within the evacuated tube and charged with positive electricity. Professor Thomson reasoned with good logic that if the particles bore any kind of electric charge (either + or —), they would be either *attracted* or *repelled* by the plate carrying the electric charge. Sure enough, the beam was found to be either attracted or repelled by the charged plate. If the plate was negatively charged, the beam or "rays" were bent away from the plate. If a positive charge was given the plate, then the beam was bent toward the plate.

Thus did the first evidence appear pointing to the idea that this mysterious ray or beam within the tube was

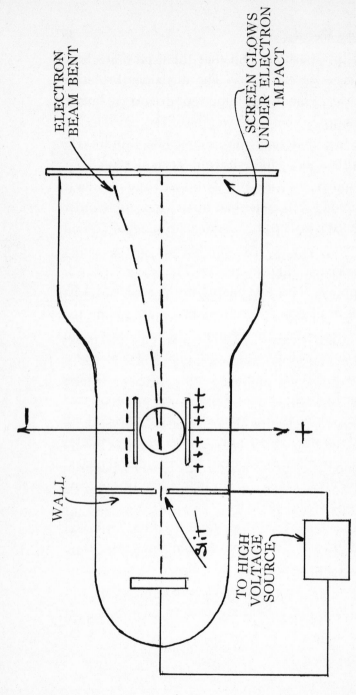

ELECTRON
BEAM BENT

SCREEN GLOWS
UNDER ELECTRON
IMPACT

WALL

Slit

TO HIGH
VOLTAGE
SOURCE

Fig. 17. Professor J. J. Thomson, using the special tube illustrated above, found that the particles making up the discharge within an evacuated tube could be diverted from their normal path by making them pass near a charged metal plate. Inasmuch as the discharge was repelled by a negative plate and attracted by a positive one, Professor Thomson decided that the particles were negatively charged. The professor also calculated their mass. The particles so discovered were later called electrons.

made up of tiny particles and that these particles bore negative charges of electricity. The ingenious Professor Thomson not only made this important discovery, but he also was able to estimate the weight of the particles, in spite of the fact that they were moving so rapidly. He knew that although a bullet moving 900 miles per hour is naturally much more difficult to *deflect* from its course than one moving 500 miles per hour, it would under certain circumstances be possible to determine the weight of an unknown bullet by measuring the amount of energy required to move it from its course. Therefore Professor Thomson applied deflective energy in the form of measured charges of electricity on the metal plate within the glass tube. The heavier the charges, the more the beam was deflected. Soon the weight of the particles was estimated and it was found that they were only 1/1840 the weight of the hydrogen atom. When it is understood that the hydrogen atom is the smallest and lightest of all atoms, it will be seen that an ultra-small piece of matter was at hand. Countless millions of them could be placed in a pile and they would still be hopelessly beyond the power of a microscope to see.

This was exciting news for science. Those who had held to the theory that Crookes and Thomson were simply witnessing a phenomenon of atoms were quite taken aback. That these particles were *not* atoms was now clear. Here was something new to man. Soon Dr.

G. Johston Stoney devised a name for the new particles. He called them electrons.

Many physicists of the day began to feel that here, perhaps, were the little bricks from which all atoms were made. These men were not far from being right. But how, many asked, could atoms be composed only of negatively charged bricks of matter when it was so well known that negatively charged bricks of matter would repel each other? That was a stickler and no one volunteered to answer it. Atoms made up of all negatively charged particles *should* blow up!

Many other physicists joined the merry chase of the newly discovered electron, and many experiments were devised in attempts to learn more about it. Professor Lenard, a German, evolved the ingenious tube shown in Fig. 18, reasoning that if these particles were sufficiently small and moved sufficiently fast, they should be able to pass through a reasonable thickness of matter. The apparatus showed him to be perfectly correct, for when the fast-moving electrons struck the aluminum window, they managed to pass through it and into the outside atmosphere. Progress here, however, became very difficult because of the presence of the billions of atoms of gases which comprise the atmosphere. Collisions were frequent, so that the little electrons found it difficult to advance more than a fraction of an inch beyond the aluminum window.

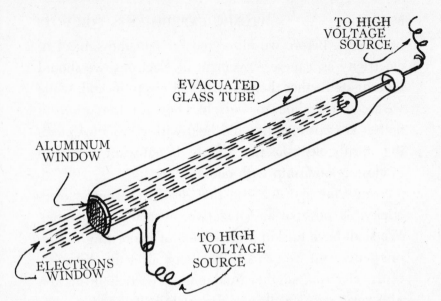

FIG. 18. By means of the arrangement shown above, Professor Lenard, a German scientist, found that electrons moving at high speed could pass through thin aluminum foil.

But where did these electrons come from? Were they torn loose from atoms, or were they just the unattached particles of matter left lying about, as one might say? Well, we may assume that both theories of their origin have some foundation in fact; but the really great discovery was that electric current itself was composed of these little particles bounding along through conductors like copper, brass, etc. When they came upon materials like glass or wax and a lot of other things, they could not get through unless they were moving at very high speed and they then crashed and roared with great flashes.

Perhaps, before we move too far into the subject of electricity as a mere movement of electrons, we should investigate further the properties of electrons and, while we are at it, find out for ourselves how it is that atoms of matter are put together and held with a group of pushing, unruly electrons that simply do not want to remain in close relationship with one another.

Some time ago, we said that *dislike* charges of electricity, as positive and negative, attracted each other. We shall have to skip a great deal of interesting history of science, but we can say that, soon after the discovery of the electron, another fundamental particle of matter, also very, very small, was discovered. It is not hard to guess that this second particle was positively charged. It simply had to be. Otherwise, we would have had no way in which to hold our theoretical atom together.

The new particle was called a proton and, in place of bearing a negative electric charge, like the electron, it bore an *exactly equal but opposite charge*. In short, it was positively charged to the same degree that the electron was negatively charged.

It was subsequently found that every atom of matter, starting with the lightest, hydrogen, and going on to the heaviest, uranium, is made up of a nucleus or center composed of protons, and that the electrons swarm around these nuclei much as the satellites swirl about the sun as the center of our solar system. Although it is not always the case, most atoms have the same number of electrons as protons, so that a balanced electrical condition prevails. Atoms where such conditions hold are always unusually stable from a chemical standpoint. On the other hand, where an atom has more protons than electrons, an electrically unbalanced condition exists. When such an atom comes upon another atom having more electrons than protons, things begin to happen chemically. Such atoms react violently with each other. In fact, today, all chemical action is regarded in the light of an interchange of electrons between atoms.

CHAPTER 4

Putting Atoms Together

INASMUCH AS THE GAS HYDROGEN IS THE
lightest substance in the world, it follows that its atom is
the smallest, the least complicated and has the least
number of particles in it. A crude diagram of the atom
of hydrogen shows a single electron (—) swinging furi-
ously around a core (called a nucleus) made up of a
single proton (+). When the science of atomics was
very young, this was the first atom put together by the
physicists. The simple structure of this atom satisfied all
of the requirements of the new theory of matter; two
particles bearing equal and oppositely charged particles.
Apparently the constant motion of the electron around
the proton prevented it from being sucked into the latter.

The curious thing about this simple arrangement was
that practically all of its weight or mass was formed by
the proton. Inasmuch as this atom was the lightest of all

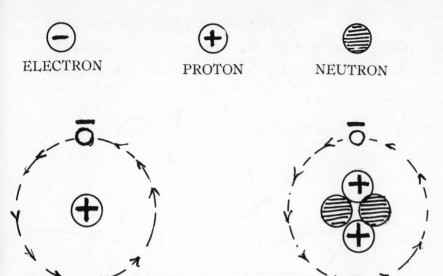

FIG. 19. The three basic particles, electron, proton, and neutron. At the lower left is a diagram of the atom of hydrogen; at the lower right, the atom of helium.

known elements of matter, it was given a mass of 1. Thus it stood at the top of the list of atoms arranged according to their atomic weights. Each succeeding atom according to this list had more electrons, protons and neutrons, the atom of hydrogen being the only atom that did not involve neutrons. (More about neutrons later.)

As the number of electrons and protons increased in the heavier atoms below hydrogen, things became pretty complicated. In the case of the very heavy atoms, such as lead, thorium, uranium, etc., physicists not only had to visualize and account for a very complex and com-

plicated bundle of protons in the core of such atoms but
they also had to arrange orbits or paths of circular motion

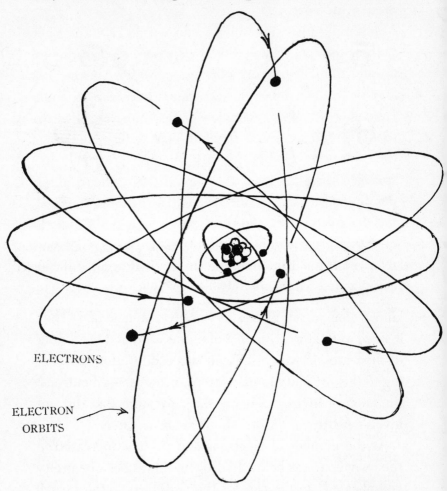

ELECTRONS

ELECTRON
ORBITS

Fig. 20.   How the electrons swirl about the core or nucleus of an atom
in orbits of increasing diameter.

about these cores for the swarm of electrons. For every proton in a core there had to be an electron whirling around the core.

Naturally these electrons could not all take the same path or the same plane. Some were supposed to revolve around the core at very close range, others farther out and still others much farther out. They were thought (and this is still so) to follow paths something like the string wound around a baseball core. Each member of the swarm traveled in its own separate orbit and at a specified distance from the core. It was a case of expanding orbits and terrific speeds. The distances separating the various electron orbits or circular paths and the core was great compared with the size of the particles involved. Thus each atom no matter how simple or how complicated was thought to be mostly empty space. This is still held. If the nucleus of a hydrogen atom was increased to the size of a baseball and the distance between it and its lonely electron was multiplied by the same factor, the electron would be about eight city blocks away.

Really every time a student of chemistry brings about a chemical reaction wherein one element combines with another to form a chemical compound, he is dealing with the subject of electronics and atomic physics, or, as many call it, nuclear physics.

Most all of the elements in the Periodic Table are

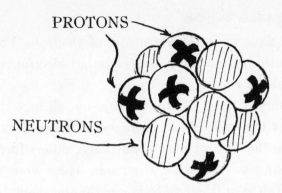

PROTONS

NEUTRONS

Fig. 21. How the neutrons and protons are packed together in the nucleus of atoms.

chemically active. By this is meant that they will enter into chemical combinations with other elements under the proper conditions. Some are so active and have such affinity or attraction for other elements that mere close association will produce an explosion as in the case of hydrogen combining with oxygen to form water. Other elements need some encouragement such as an application of heat to form unions. Still others are so perfectly balanced electrically speaking that they refuse combination. The gas helium is such an element. These unsociable elements are said to be inert. Oftentimes the words stable and unstable are used.

Chemical affinity or attraction between the elements is now known to be due to what have become known as "valence electrons" in the outer orbits of atoms. When chemical combination takes place in a chemical reaction, the outer loose electrons of one element become associated with the electrons in the outer orbit of another element. Thus an electrically binding union is produced. Roughly, this is the mechanism of the whole science of chemistry.

It is the neutron alone, however, that brings about the so-called chain-reaction which amounts to the explosion of one atom being quickly communicated to other adjacent atoms. These in turn explode other atoms, etc. Although we will have more to say about the chain reaction in a later Chapter, our accompanying diagram provides a crude idea of the mechanism involved.

In the early day of the electron or nuclear theory of matter certain very disturbing irregularities were noticed especially when the elements were arranged in the order of their atomic weights and the Periodic Table.

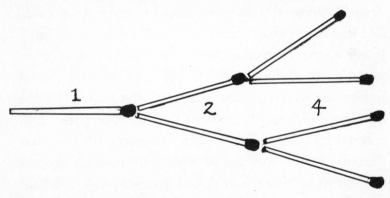

Fig. 22. Crude diagram showing the principle of the chain reaction. When match No. 1 is lighted, it will set off two more and these will set off four more, etc.

The hydrogen atom being made up of a single electron and a single proton was assumed to have a unit weight of 1. Serious difficulty began right away when the next-to-lightest element, the gas helium, was placed next to hydrogen where it apparently belonged. Helium had therefore an atomic number of 2. Its atom was supposed to have 2 protons and 2 electrons. However, the two protons would give it an atomic weight of only 2 whereas it actually had an atomic weight of 4. In short, it had an additional mass of 2 that could not be accounted for.

What was true of helium, turned out to be true of all of the elements. Carbon, for example, had an atomic number of 6 but an atomic weight of 12. That left six protons accounted for. Every element listed beyond hydrogen appeared to have an atomic weight about twice as large as its atomic number. In the case of the very heavy element uranium, its atomic number of 92 compared to its atomic weight of 238. Two decades passed before this mystery was solved. The physicists of the day developed a theory to account for this discrepancy that was not far from the mark. They advanced the idea that the extra weight was due to neutralized protons; protons that for some reason had pulled in an electron and held it, the negative electron neutralizing the equal but opposite positive charge of the proton. The geniuses of nuclear research knew that this was a sloppy answer that left certain other questions still unanswered but that it would have to do until the problem was solved.

Really the so-called neutralized proton, supposed to be a close union of one proton and one electron, had to be viewed as a sort of collapsed atom of hydrogen. Uranium was thought to have 92 regular protons and 146 neutralized protons. Ninety-two regular protons plus 146 neutralized protons were equal to an atomic weight of 238; a speculation that at least temporarily brought a degree of peace and comfort to the minds of the men at work in the field.

This mystery of the neutralized proton lasted for some twenty years, before the Englishman, John Chadwick, came forth with an answer in 1932. While bombarding the light element, beryllium, with alpha rays (or particles) from radium, Chadwick found that fragments of beryllium atoms were released which were, we might

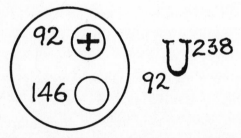

Fɪɢ. 23. Diagrammatic representation of the atom of Uranium 238. The black circle marked 146 relates to the number of neutrons present in this atom.

say, pretty wild. When alpha particles (rays) or electrons
(beta rays when they were discharged from matter) were
exposed to powerful electrical or magnetic effects, such
particles behaved in a certain predictable manner. They
were always deflected from their courses of motion. This
was not so with the new particles that Chadwick had
blasted out of beryllium. They not only traveled very
slowly but they were unaffected by either powerful magnets or powerful electric charges and, even though slow
in motion, they appeared to be able to penetrate matter
with the greatest of ease. The fact that these newly
observed particles penetrated matter with ease and were
unaffected both by electrical charges and powerful magnetic fields showed that the particle was electrically neutral. Indeed it was not long before Chadwick proved
conclusively that here was the particle that solved the
mystery of atomic weights. It was found, like the charged
proton, to have a mass of 1. It was not, however, a collapsed atom of hydrogen; it had no electron attached to
it. It was simply a proton without charge of any kind.
It was christened "neutron."

The atoms of all the elements then had to be viewed
in a new light; another particle, the neutron, had to be
admitted to every atomic nucleus or core save the atom
of simple hydrogen. Helium had 2 protons and 2 neutrons, carbon had 6 protons and 6 neutrons, barium had
56 protons and 81 neutrons, etc.

It was not known at the time but the neutron was the most potent atomic bullet yet discovered. When charged particles like electrons or protons were fired into the nuclei of atoms they met with other electrical forces that might reject them or accept them with little or no effect. *The neutron, however, bore no electric charge whatever and it could therefore enter even the cores of the heaviest and most complex atoms with the greatest of ease. Once inside, however, it was found that it could cause great havoc. The neutron was the bullet that made the release of atomic energy possible.*

While it is quite true that no less than 19 atomic particles are now known, it is also true that the functions of some of these are not understood. For our own purposes, we can cling to the three particles discussed up to this point, the electron (—), the proton (+) and the electrically neutral neutron.

CHAPTER 5

Energy, the Ghost
of Matter

AFTER THE DISCOVERY OF RADIUM BY MAD-
ame Curie and her husband Pierre (1898) physicists
were at a loss to understand what was really taking place.
Here was a very complex atom of matter that was constantly troubled with a sort of indigestion. It was
constantly "burping" and nothing, no force available to
man no matter how powerful, could settle its atomic
stomach or nucleus. Always, even under the most extreme
conditions of heat, cold or pressure, it was shooting off
its own substances in the form of gamma or x-rays, electrons (—) and alpha particles (+) which were in truth
atoms of the second lightest element, the gas helium.
Further to complicate this strange performance radium
was always slightly warmer than its surroundings proving that it was also producing heat waves.

As we might surmise, each atom of radium, upon the completion of the mysterious process, was lighter in weight and certain complicated rearrangements of its nucleus were taking place. After a long series of such readjustments taking eons of time, the atoms of radium finally became atoms of the stable element lead. Scientists rightfully surmised that during these strange capers of the atoms of radium part of their mass or weight was being converted into released energy. It was during these years that the scientists began to realize that matter could be converted into energy and that atoms were indeed explosive. Of course, radium was exploding very slowly something like a bunch of wet firecrackers. What might happen, the scientists were asking themselves, if a really fast or instantaneous explosion could be arranged and all of this slowly released energy could be released in a small fraction of a second? The delicate instruments used in the early days of atomic research along with mathematics demonstrated beyond a question of doubt that, compared with the amounts of matter involved, atomic explosions were far more powerful than anything that had been dreamed of before.

If we could gather in and weigh all of the chemical products produced by an explosion of gunpowder, TNT or dynamite, we would find that the total weight of such products matched perfectly the weight of the gunpowder, TNT or dynamite that we started with. This was not true with exploding atoms. Somewhere, somehow a part of the mass of the atom completely disappeared. Matter became energy. It began to appear that there was a strange relationship between the two.

Further to tease the minds of the men at work on the problem was the fact that when electrons were speeded up, their weight or mass increased. Here was the reverse of the mass-into-energy mystery. This was energy-into-mass. To speed up an electron, one had to apply energy to it just as in the speeding up of an automobile. This energy (electrical) applied to electrons showed up as increased weight. An electron traveling 20,000 miles per second weighed less than an electron traveling 50,000 miles per second. This business of energy-vs.-matter worked both ways.

Before 1885, physicists never dreamed that there was a relationship between an ounce of matter and a unit of energy such as an ampere, a horsepower, a watt, a calorie or a B.T.U. No one had thought of matter in terms of energy much less energy in terms of matter. Matter converted into energy? Nonsense, most scientists would have said. Perhaps even the great Einstein himself never dared to dream of the atomic bomb or the atomic pile. Many years of patient research were necessary to move his famous formula $E = mc^2$ from the realm of theory into the realm of physical law and practical things. (More about $E = mc^2$ later.)

If we will return to the simple atom of helium which holds 2 protons and 2 neutrons within its nucleus, perhaps we can learn something more about this strange matter-energy relationship. When scientists got around to making very accurate measurements of the mass or weight of the proton and the neutron, a curious thing happened. The business was not quite as simple as it was first thought to be. The nucleus of helium (we must remember that electrons weigh so little that it is the nucleus of each atom that makes up most of its mass) was found not to be an exact multiple of the weights of the 2 protons and 2 neutrons that made it up. The nucleus turned out to be too light by a small fraction. Somehow or other it seemed that when nature put the atom of helium together part of the mass of the nucleus apparently disappeared in the form of energy.

Where did it go? Did it "dissolve" into energy as Dr. Albert Einstein's mathematical formula (1905) might have suggested? Even at that early date the great genius, Einstein, suggested mathematically that energy and matter were simply two aspects of the same thing. It was then that he evolved his famous, world-shaking but simple formula $E = mc^2$ where E equals energy, m = mass and c the speed of light. While many scientists did not at the time agree with Dr. Einstein, the terrible truth became evident when the first atomic bomb was exploded. Einstein's mathematical formula is probably the most important ever written within the history of man.

Now let us return to the discrepancy in the weight of the helium nucleus. First it was found by precise measurements that the mass of the proton was not exactly 1 but 1.00758 and that the neutron was 1.00893 or practically the same. Inasmuch as the nucleus of helium was made up of protons and 2 neutrons, it would follow on the basis of fourth-grade arithmetic that the protons of the helium nucleus would have a total mass of 2 $\times$ 1.00758 or 2.01516 and that the total mass of the neutrons would be 2 $\times$ 1.00893 or 2.01786. Thus to reach the total mass of the nucleus of the helium atom we would have only to add 2.01516 (protons) to 2.01786 (neutrons). The sum of these two figures would be 4.03302, the total mass of the nucleus. However, the total mass of the nucleus of the helium atom was found not to be 4.03302 but 4.00280 which was a little lighter than the theoretical figure and which made a difference of .03022. It was this small fraction (approximately ¾ of 1%) of mass that had somehow or other disappeared when nature assembled the atom of helium. Where did it go?

In terms of nuclear energy as it is now known, a mass of .03022 is not to be ignored. This small fraction of the mass of a few billion atoms suddenly released beneath our chair could be very disastrous.

Reduced to more simple terms, this discrepancy in mass amounted to 3 in every 400 parts. If this energy in

1 gram (1/20th of an ounce) of helium at the moment of formation from hydrogen was translated into electrical terms it would keep 200,000 100-watt electric bulbs burning for 10 hours! When it comes to mass-energy relationship, we cannot discount even the small amount of matter that can be piled on the head of a pin.

Some nuclear physicists now believe that the tremendous heat constantly generated in our great solar furnace, the sun, is produced by the union of 2 atoms of hydrogen to form 1 atom of helium.

Apparently whenever atomic or nuclear energy is released, the atomic nuclei left behind in a rearranged condition as a result of the explosion are always in a more stable and peaceful state. It seems that nature is always seeking a sort of neutralism where her atoms will be more stable and better behaved. Sometimes, as in the case of radium, the condition of stability is not always reached by a single rearrangement but through a long series of rearrangements.

It has been stated before that atoms vary greatly in weight and in complexity. As atoms grow heavier they also grow more complicated and some of them less stable. Still another factor of great interest to nuclear physicists is the degree to which the neutrons and protons of a nucleus are packed together in the core or nucleus of the atom. More important still our nuclear physicists were confused for a long time as to the manner in which the protons and neutrons of a nucleus were kept so tightly packed together. After all, the neutrons bore no electric charge of any kind and the protons were all positively charged. Knowing as we do from reading the early part of this book that like or similar charges of electricity repel or push each other, we cannot help but wonder how this neat little package of the atom nucleus does not explode automatically or, more sensible yet, how it was put together in the first place. Two positively charged ping-pong balls repel or push each other when they are brought together, why not protons? Does the presence of the neutrons prevent it? After all, every atom save hydrogen with its single proton and no neutron is the only exception. Immediately we find nuclei with more than one proton we begin to find almost balancing numbers of neutrons. Do these neutrons prevent the electrically hostile protons from flying apart?

As yet no one appears to have the perfect answer to that problem and the theories advanced are too involved and complex to be outlined in this book.

At this point, however, we may pause to give thought to one interesting fact that may not have occurred to us before. We have just learned that when two atoms of hydrogen combine to form an atom of helium, mass is given off in the form of energy. In short energy can be given off during the structure of atoms or the building up of heavier substances from light components.

Radium and other radioactive elements reverse this process. They are constantly breaking down and losing weight and a small percentage of this weight or mass is converted into energy. Thus it would seem that by a process of addition during the build-up of atoms energy is released and that it is also released during the tearing apart of atoms.

The amount of energy released by the conversion of matter when atoms are formed or when they are broken down depends upon what nuclear physicists called the "packing factor" and the "packing factor" has been worked out for each element, starting with hydrogen as zero because hydrogen, having only a single proton in its nucleus could not have such a factor. There is not only the packing factor of atoms but also something the physicists call the "binding energy." This is the energy that is emitted during atomic explosions of all kinds. A full treatment of this angle of our subject, however, might prove too confusing.

CHAPTER 6

Atomic Cousins:
the Isotopes

UP TO THE PRESENT WE HAVE BEEN DEALING principally with the simplest atoms in nature, the atoms of hydrogen and helium. As atoms grow in size and mass (weight) they also grow in complexity and the number of protons, neutrons and electrons they contain.

All of the elements of matter of which we have around 95 (the basic substances of the earth) are arranged according to the weight in what is known as the Periodic Table. Here we begin with the lightest atom or element, hydrogen, and wind up with the heaviest atom, uranium.

The nuclear physicists arrange their atoms in the same manner except that they introduce another figure. In the case of uranium they write $_{92}U^{238}$. The 238 represents the atomic weight, the 92 indicates not only the number of protons in the nucleus but the position of the atom in the Periodic Table as well. Along with the 92 protons in the uranium nucleus, there are also 146 neutrons. By adding 146 neutrons to 92 protons, we have a total of 238, which is the atomic weight.

Carbon, for instance, has an atomic weight of 12 because it has 6 protons and 6 neutrons in its nucleus; $6 + 6 = 12$. Carbon is indicated by $_6C^{12}$. The lithium atom has 3 protons and 4 neutrons in its nucleus. Lithium therefore has an atomic weight of 7. And so it goes.

If we were advanced students of the atom, however, we would discover that this Periodic Table is not quite as simple as it seems. In a large number of places between the elements listed we would have to insert what we might call the cousins of some of the atoms listed. These are atoms that are practically but not quite the same. For instance, we really have three different kinds of atoms of hydrogen. There is (1) just plain, everyday hydrogen which we breathe and with which we fill balloons. Such common hydrogen is represented by H^1 by our chemists and nuclear physicists. Then there is another form of hydrogen (2) represented by the symbol H^2. Whereas ordinary hydrogen has an atomic weight roughly represented by 1, the second form of hydrogen has an atomic weight of 2. After this form of hydrogen was discovered (in the early 1930's) it was called deuterium and its nucleus or core was called a deuteron. This so-called "heavy hydrogen" was not a new element in nature, only a newly discovered one. Wherever ordinary light hydrogen was present so was heavy hydrogen. For every atom of heavy hydrogen there were 5000 atoms of common hydrogen. When most of the common atoms of hydrogen in water (H_2O) were gathered up and carried away by a special process the resulting liquid was called "heavy water"; it weighed more than ordinary water.

There is still another form (3) of heavy hydrogen; heavier still than deuterium. This was called tritium and is now represented by the symbol H^3. In Fig. 24, we note that all three forms of hydrogen have but one lonely electron swinging around their nuclei.

Such variations in nuclear arrangements are called isotopes. We might call them atomic cousins so closely are they related each to the other. Many of the chemical elements listed in the Periodic Table have atomic cousins or isotopes. Some occur in nature and are associated with the ordinary element in very small degrees. Still others are produced artificially by bombardment in cyclotrons or atomic piles. In such cases isotopic variation is forced upon the nucleus of atoms and as a result a sort of nuclear indigestion is produced and such nuclei are apt to "burp." They are unstable and tend to rearrange themselves in such a manner as to overcome their indigestion. For instance, in the case of carbon, which has three forms, two natural and the other artificially produced in the atomic pile, the first natural isotope having 7 neutrons

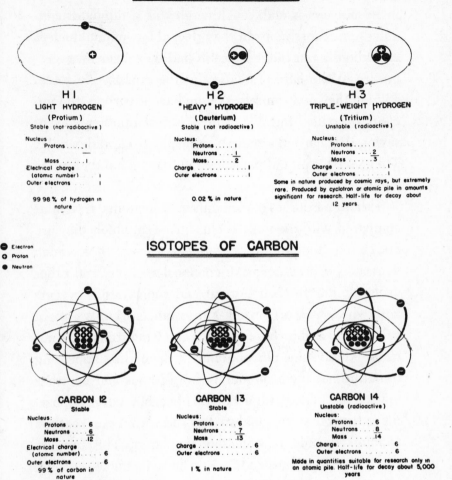

ISOTOPES OF HYDROGEN

H I
LIGHT HYDROGEN
(Protium)
Stable (not radioactive)

Nucleus
Protons I
―
Mass I
Electrical charge
(atomic number) . . . I
Outer electrons . . . I

99.98 % of hydrogen in
nature

H 2
"HEAVY" HYDROGEN
(Deuterium)
Stable (not radioactive)

Nucleus:
Protons I
Neutrons I
Mass 2
Charge I
Outer electrons I

0.02 % in nature

H 3
TRIPLE-WEIGHT HYDROGEN
(Tritium)
Unstable (radioactive)

Nucleus:
Protons I
Neutrons 2
Mass 3
Charge I
Outer electrons I

Some in nature produced by cosmic rays, but extremely
rare. Produced by cyclotron or atomic pile in amounts
significant for research. Half-life for decay about
12 years

ISOTOPES OF CARBON

● Electron
◐ Proton
● Neutron

CARBON 12
Stable

Nucleus:
Protons 6
Neutrons 6
Mass 12
Electrical charge
(atomic number) 6
Outer electrons 6
99 % of carbon in
nature

CARBON 13
Stable

Nucleus:
Protons 6
Neutrons 7
Mass 13
Charge 6
Outer electrons 6

I % in nature

CARBON 14
Unstable (radioactive)

Nucleus:
Protons 6
Neutrons . . . 8
Mass 14
Charge 6
Outer electrons 6

Made in quantities suitable for research only in
an atomic pile. Half-life for decay about 5,000
years

FIG. 24.   (Top) The arrangements of the atom of hydrogen and its two
isotopes H₂ and H₃. (Bottom) The atomic arrangements of Carbon 12,
13, and 14.

in its nucleus is stable. Although this arrangement involves one more neutron than does the common nucleus of carbon, a fair balance is still had. However, when exposure to the fierce radiation of the atomic pile forces still another neutron into the nucleus of carbon, the nucleus becomes unstable, which is just another way of saying that carbon atoms so altered become radioactive. They seek to spit out particles and reach a point of peace and quiet.

Although isotopes of elements vary in atomic weight as compared with the normal element with which they are associated, the differences appear to end there. Such variations or isotopes have chemical and physical properties similar to their normal and more basic brothers with which they are mixed. For instance, what we might call normal carbon has 6 protons and 6 neutrons in its nucleus. Ninety-nine percent of all of the carbon appearing in nature has the same number of protons and neutrons in its atoms. The natural isotope of carbon never appearing in the free state but always mixed with normal carbon amounts to only 1 percent of the latter. This form of carbon has 6 protons and 7 neutrons in its nucleus. When exposure to the radiation of an atomic pile causes an additional neutron to slither into the nucleus of the carbon atom (making 8 neutrons with still only 6 protons), that appears to create an out-of-balance condition that automatically brings about radioactivity.

It has now long been known that chemical activity between the various elements and compounds is caused by exchanges of electrons in the outer orbits of atoms; valence electrons they are called. Following this fact, we can easily understand why it is that the isotopes of an element display the same chemical properties as the basic element itself. Although the first isotope of carbon has 7 neutrons as compared with 6 for the basic element and the second isotope has 8, the number of protons and electrons in all three atoms are the same, 6 protons and 6 electrons each. This explains why it is that, although the isotopes vary in atomic weight, they have the same chemical properties. Because neutrons bear no electric charge, we would not expect them to upset the relationship or the number of protons ($+$) and electrons ($-$) in an atom when they invade its nucleus. Isotopes involve only neutrons.

Quite aside from the artificially created isotopes now produced in atomic piles, there are some 270 that occur in nature and 670 in all. Some elements have as many as 8, some only one. All isotopes, while more numerous than the basic elements listed in the Periodic Table, make up an extremely small percentage of the matter in the world.

The artificial creation of radioactive isotopes in the atomic pile through neutron bombardment and capture (by the nucleus of atoms so exposed) is turning out to be one of the most promising research by-products of the atomic energy program. Such mildly radioactive substances are being used now in medical research and even in the treatment of certain disorders. As a research tool they are very important because they can be traced through the human system.

For reasons that we do not need to discuss here, nuclear physicists estimate the radioactivity of isotopes (isotopes are not all radioactive) in terms of half-life, this period being that needed for the radioactivity to reach half-life in the process of decay. This figure may range from less than a millionth of a second to billions of years. Perhaps a better idea of what is meant by half-life will be had by imagining a piece of ice, half of which melts each day. It will be only half as big tomorrow as it is today, and one quarter as big the day after tomorrow as it is today, etc. Each day it is half as big as it was the day previous. It could be said, then, that the piece of ice has a half-life of one day.

CHAPTER 7

Watching Atomic Bullets and Explosions

FOR LITTLE OR NOTHING, THE YOUNG ATOMIC researcher may make one of the most fascinating atomic instruments of all. With it he may see the dazzling effects left by exploding atoms. Most of the simple materials needed for this marvelous instrument (called a spinthariscope and invented by Sir William Crookes in 1903) can be found about the house.

First we must make a small telescoping cardboard box as shown in Fig. 25. This is cut from fairly heavy cardboard and scored with a sharp knife where it is bent. To add strength at the corners and joints, we reinforce these points with gummed paper tape. However, before the box is assembled, we cover the inside surfaced with dull black paint.

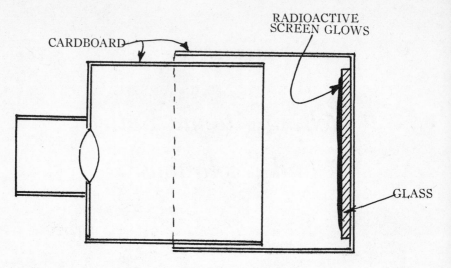

CARDBOARD

RADIOACTIVE
SCREEN GLOWS

GLASS

Fig. 25. Diagram of a simple homemade spinthariscope. The glass at the extreme right inside the cardboard container is coated with a mixture of radioactive material and zinc sulphide. This sparkles when viewed through the opposite end of the box. The sparkling is due to atomic explosions in the radioactive material.

In the viewing end of the box we cut a small round hole and mount a small magnifying lens (double convex) over it by means of model airplane cement. The size of the lens is not important nor is its power. Whatever the power, the telescoping box will permit focusing.

When the atoms of radioactive materials explode in the presence of certain chemical compounds, a phenomenon known as phosphorescence takes place. Really phosphorescence amounts to visible light produced when such compounds are bombarded by disintegrating radioactive particles. Under conditions of total darkness, the

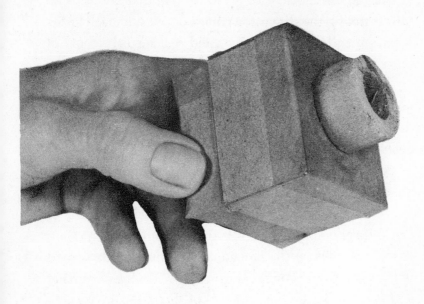

FIG. 26. The complete homemade spinthariscope illustrated in the accompanying drawing.

startling effects of such atomic explosions may be clearly seen in the dark.

The radioactive material needed to charge the spinthariscope is neither costly or difficult to procure. Indeed if we have a discarded alarm clock with a radium dial about the house, we will have enough radioactive material to make a dozen spinthariscopes, each one capable of lasting thousands of years beyond the lifetime of the builder.

If an alarm clock with a radioactive dial is not to be found among the discarded things of our home, then the local secondhand store may yield one for fifty cents or more especially if it is in need of repair.

We simply remove the dial and scrape off the radioactive paint from a number or two with a sharp knife, permitting the removed material to fall upon a piece of clean glass.

To this we add a gram of powdered phosphorescent zinc sulphide which may be had for a small amount from any chemical supply house. Using the clean blade of the knife as a spatula, we mix the two powders together. After such mixing, the flat side of the knife blade is used with pressure to produce a grinding as well as a mixing action. This will reduce the size of the radioactive particles scraped off the clock dial and mix them thoroughly with the zinc sulphide powder.

Next a small piece of glass is cut so that it will fit inside the cardboard box. If a glass cutter is not at hand, a splinter of glass will do just as well. It is used only to hold the mixture of radioactive powder and the zinc sulphide. The powder mixture is held to the surface of the glass by first covering the latter with a film of clear varnish or shellac. After this is tacky (the glass is laid flat or horizontal) the mixture is sprinkled upon it.

As a measure of precaution it is best that we do not directly handle the radioactive material scraped off the clock dial or indeed permit it to come in contact with our skin at any point. To distribute it on the tacky varnish surface, we brush the mixed powder from the glass upon which it was prepared onto a piece of gauze held over the tacky varnish.

This done, the gauze is agitated so that the fine powder will sift through and fall upon the tacky varnish or shellac in as even a coating as possible after which the varnish or shellac is left to harden.

As a matter of further precaution, we should thereafter wash our hands with soap and water and scrub them with a brush.

The coated glass is glued powdered side out to the bottom of the box at the end opposite the lens. Model airplane cement may be used for this.

The cardboard or wooden rim around the lens is put in place to shade the eye and to keep out as much extraneous light as possible while the viewing is done. The effects of the atomic explosions taking place are best seen in total darkness. Some optical adjustment of our viewing eye must also take place before these atomic pyrotechnics can be observed. Therefore we should not be too impatient. It may take the better part of a minute before the pupil of the eye has adjusted itself to the darkness and the bright flashes that appear like twinkling stars are seen. Here is matter exploding before our very eyes and these explosions will go on for thousands and thousands of years. More wonderful still perhaps is the fact that we can do nothing to stop them. We could dash our little spinthariscope into the furnace and consume it completely by fire but the atoms of the radioactive material, although separated, would go right on exploding as though nothing had happened.

What we see here are the effects produced when atoms of radium break down or decompose, a process that goes on for countless centuries until the radium is turned into lead. Once this speck of radium that amuses us was uranium but that was a few billion years ago! Uranium, like radium, also has explosive atoms that change into atoms of lighter metals. Really this disintegration or decomposition is not quite as simple as this because a whole series of intermediate stages are reached but the result is as first stated. The whole process amounts to slow, automatic transmutation (changing one basic element of matter into another) established by nature and with nature only able to extinguish it.

If we had a teaspoonful of fresh radium (usually radium chloride or radium bromide) 52,000,000,000 radium atoms would burst every second of time and yet the atoms are so small that this process could go on for 1600 years before half the atoms had exploded. The amounts involved make no difference. The one ten millionth of a gram that we scraped off the dial of the alarm clock will be just as long-lived as a tub full.

But what really causes these tiny, myriad flashes of light as we peek into the darkness of the spinthariscope? The atoms of radium "blow-up" and they shoot off free electrons (these are called beta rays when they come from radium) atoms of helium (these are called alpha particles) and x-rays (called gamma rays). It is the so-called alpha particles or the atoms of helium that cause the zinc sulphide to become phosphorescent or to give off visible light. The alpha particles move with a speed of about 12,000 miles per second. One milligram of radium ($\frac{1}{28000}$th of an ounce) shoots off no less than 126,000,000 alpha particles per second.

For best results, we should be in a dark room for about five minutes before we peek into this magic box. This permits the pupils of our eyes to adjust themselves for seeing.

CHAPTER 8

Miracle in a Pickle Jar

ATOMS MUCH LESS THAN THE PARTICLES THAT go to make them up have never been seen. Indeed there is little chance that they will ever come within the range of vision. Because of this many junior students of the atom wonder how we have learned so much about things that are so hopelessly small and invisible.

This knowledge has been slowly put together over the past sixty-five years by the use of some of the most ingenious instruments ever devised by man. A few of these marvelous devices are so simple that we may assemble and use them at home. The wonderful Wilson cloud chamber has taught our scientists of the atom many things about the nature of atomic particles. Along with the Geiger counter, the cyclotron and the electroscope it has been one of the key instruments used in the war on the atom.

If our eyes were powerful enough to see, we would find ourselves in a very confused and busy world atomically speaking. From all sides, including the sky, we would be bombarded by atomic particles many of them moving at speeds of thousands of miles per second. Mysterious cosmic-ray particles are constantly bombarding us from outer space. Atomic explosions are taking place in apparently peaceful pieces of ore bearing radioactive materials and particles are always being emitted by the luminous dials of wrist watches and alarm clocks.

Now under certain and very peculiar conditions the movement and direction of these particles can be seen. This is done in a device invented many years ago by a Scotsman, Professor C. T. R. Wilson. In it we can see electrons and other sub-atomic particles "on the run."

Professional type Wilson cloud chambers, still widely used in atomic research, are very expensive and very complicated. Months of instruction would be required before we could learn to operate such a thing. Thanks to the physicists working at the Brookhaven National Laboratory, we may now not only assemble such a device on the kitchen table but use it there to watch the tiny, luminous paths, like miniature streaks of lightning, left by sub-atomic.particles in passing through a special atmosphere.

We have already been told that such particles have

certain electrical properties; that is they are either positive, negative or electrically neutral in nature. In a certain
type of atmosphere (air) artificially created in, say, an
old pickle jar, the passage of such particles will leave a
certain kind of condensation in their wake no matter how
rapid their motion may be. With the right kind of powerful illumination, we will be able to see the tiny streaks
of condensed moisture left behind.

Perhaps we can understand this business better if
we recall that rainfall on the earth has much to do with
small electrified particles (not atoms or sub-atomic particles, however,) acting as the nuclei (center) of rain-
drops. It was this knowledge of the causes of rain that
made artificial rain making possible.

Now for the construction of our cloud chamber. First
we will need a wide-mouthed glass jar of about 1 pt.
capacity or larger. This should have a metal screw top
and some form of seal that will be tight. If such a seal is
not supplied with the metal top then we can make one
by cutting a circle of rubber from an old inner tube and
cementing it into the inside of the metal jar top (see
drawing, Fig. 27). Over this rubber disc we glue a piece
of black velvet having a diameter slightly less than the
rubber disc. This is to permit the edges of the rubber to
contact the lip of the glass jar when the top is screwed
down. The circle of black velvet has no purpose other
than that of permitting us to see better. The telltale

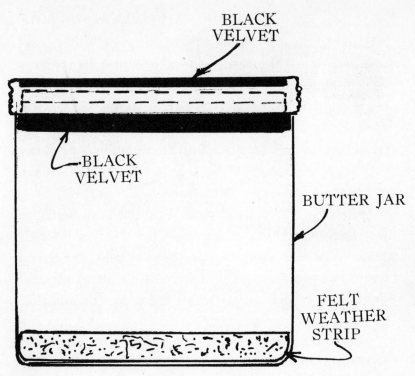

BLACK
VELVET

BLACK
VELVET

BUTTER JAR

FELT
WEATHER
STRIP

Fig. 27. Simple construction details of a Wilson cloud chamber in which the paths of atomic and cosmic ray particles may be seen.

paths of the atomic particles are best viewed against a black background.

To complete our chamber of atomic wonders we will need a foot or two of ordinary felt weatherstrip obtainable at any five-and-ten-cent store. One strip of this felt is cemented to the inside upper rim of the jar and one around the bottom of the jar. If possible rubber or airplane cement is used for this purpose.

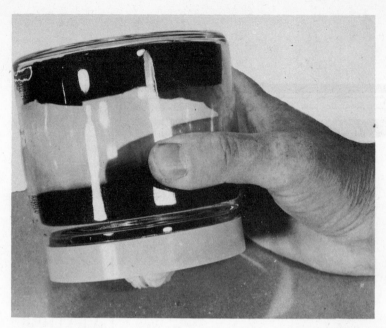

FIG. 28. The complete Wilson cloud chamber in a glass jar.

Next we will need a one-pound coffee can, some methyl alcohol, a roll of clean cotton and some dry ice which may often be obtained at ice-cream parlors. We will also need a powerful beam-type flashlight or a slide or motion-picture projector if one is about the house. We wish neither to project movies or slides but to simply use one of these machines to illuminate the inside of the chamber. In any case the source of light is placed very close to the jar in an otherwise perfectly dark room but not before the following preparations are made:

First we pour in enough alcohol completely to saturate (fill) the felt strip around the bottom of the jar with

FIG. 29. How the Wilson cloud chamber is set up for use with a cake of dry ice and a source of illumination.

enough to spare to leave a pool ⅛th inch deep. The cover of the jar complete with the black velvet inside covering is then tightly screwed into place and the jar is inverted, thereby permitting the excess alcohol in the bottom to be soaked up by the felt band in the upper section of the glass jar.

Still upside down, the jar is then placed on a cake of dry ice resting on a wad of cotton batting in a pound metal coffee can. If the light source is now brought close to the glass jar and we watch with care, a relatively short vigil will reward us with the thrilling sight of the luminous path left by an electrified atomic particle. When such a particle passes through the alcohol vapor atmosphere within the jar. This atmosphere is then in a condition known as "saturated." By this we mean that there is so much alcohol in the atmosphere that it can hold no more. Indeed there is so much alcohol present and the molecules of alcohol are so crowded that they are looking for a chance to condense or come still closer together which they cannot do unless a certain trigger action, we might say, takes place. This trigger action is supplied by the passage of an electrified atomic particle. Alcohol molecules close in and huddle more closely upon such a passage and it is this streak of bunched alcohol molecules that we see rather than the atomic particle itself.

But how, we ask, are such particles going to reach the interior of our glass wonder chamber when it is closed and sealed? We might as well ask how particles carried by the wind pass through a chicken-wire fence. The spaces separating the atoms and molecules comprising the glass of the jar are so great compared with the size of molecules and atoms that the tiny particles comprising cosmic rays easily pass between them. Thus the ray particles constantly bombarding the earth from outer space gain admittance to the simple cloud chamber and make their presence visible through condensation.

The purpose of the cold supplied by the dry ice is simply that of bringing alcohol vapor to a point very near condensation; a point so close to it that the job is completed by the small electrical charge supplied by the passage of an electrically charged particle. Every intelligent boy knows that a lowering of temperature produces condensation in the case of water vapor. That is the reason for wet windows in the kitchen during wintertime when mother is making soup on the kitchen range.

Those among us who have seen meteors or "shooting stars" will be reminded of them when we witness the passage of cosmic-ray particles through the magic showcase of our homemade cloud chamber.

The condensed alcohol left in the wake of each passing cosmic particle is called a "track" by our nuclear physicists. If we watch our magic chamber closely we will notice the rhythmic appearance of these tracks every second or so. Some of these cosmic particles we will be

Fig. 30.   How particles and rays appear in the Wilson cloud chamber: (1) Alpha particle. (2) Gamma Rays. (3) Beta particles.

watching move with such speed and power that they plunge to a depth of twenty miles within our earth before they are stopped.

The Wilson cloud chamber has permitted our atomic scientists to discover many things about cosmic rays and atomic particles of all kinds. For one thing, the cloud chamber permits us to study the passages of high-speed particles through matter of various kinds and various thicknesses.

CHAPTER 9

Making Your Own
Geiger Counter

IF OUR EYES WERE LARGE ENOUGH, OR POW-erful enough to see, we would witness a thick, heavy rain of sub-atomic particles reaching the earth from outer space. Twenty particles composing such rays pass into our bodies (on the average, that is) every second of time. Scientists have called this form of radiation "Cosmic Rays" because they reach us from the space outside the earth's atmosphere. Most of the particles comprising cosmic rays are known to scientists because they are also associated with earthly atoms. All nuclear physicists are therefore interested in cosmic radiation.

Fortunately for the young experimenter with atoms there is a relatively simple instrument that can be assembled in any cellar workshop or even on the kitchen table and that will detect not only the high-speed cosmic rays (particles) reaching the earth from outer space but also the particles pushed out of—shall we say "local" atoms?— here on earth. For instance, if we bring a radium-dial watch or clock near this instrument it will indicate great activity.

The instrument, called a Geiger-Mueller counter after the men who invented and perfected it, is no more complicated than a small one-or-two-tube radio receiver. Many standard radio parts are used in its construction and the particular instrument about to be described was perfected by the Atomic Energy Commission especially for the construction and use by boys of high-school age. It can be used not only for laboratory radiation experiments but also for counting cosmic particles and for exploration in search of uranium deposits in the earth.

Of all of the instruments used in the field of nuclear research, the Geiger-Mueller device is the most common. Thousands of them are now employed not only in research and prospecting for uranium deposits but also as watch dogs in the manufacture of nuclear products that may be too "hot" (too radioactive, that is) for the safety of workers.

When exposed to radiation that is too intense for human safety, the Geiger-Mueller counter will give alarm either by indications on a meter, by means of sound in a rapid series of load clicks or by flashes with a neon tube.

The sensitive element of a Geiger-Mueller counter takes the form of a special but very simple gas-filled glass tube with two metal electrodes sealed within it. Cosmic or nuclear particles pass through the glass envelope of the tube and cause certain very delicate electrical effects between the electrodes or plates inside the tube. These effects are so small that were it not for certain delicately balanced radio and electronic components there would be no method of making their presence known. With such instruments properly connected to the counter tube itself, however, every particle entering the sensitive tube can be made to produce either a flash of red light in a neon tube or a sound in the form of a loud click, the click being produced either in a headphone or a loud-speaker. The number of clicks coming in each second of time will indicate the intensity of the radiation.

The action that takes place within a Geiger-Mueller tube is not difficult to understand. Each time an atomic particle passes through the glass tube it produces what is known as a "pulse." These pulses may be indicated not only by sound or flashes but also on what is known as a "rate meter"; a special electrical meter calibrated in terms of atomic radiation.

Fig. 31 illustrates the Geiger-Mueller tube principle. Its vital elements amount only to two metal electrodes, one a cylinder and the other a wire running through the center of the metal cylinder or tube. A relatively high

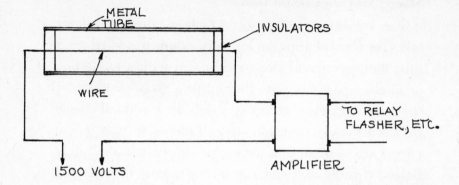

FIG. 31. Simple principle of the Geiger counter. When a cosmic or radiation particle flashes across the small space between the wire and the metal tube, a small amount of electricity is made to flow between these members. This is amplified and then made either to cause a click in a loudspeaker or a telephone, or to make a small light flash. Sometimes electrical counters are attached to such instruments.

voltage is connected to the wire and the tube but inasmuch as these elements are electrically insulated from each other, no current will flow between them.

Such tubes are also filled with certain gases and when a high-speed particle enters such tubes, it passes through the metal cylinder and proceeds on its way to the control wire electrode. However, when the electrified particle passes through the gas it ionizes it or charges many of the gas molecules or atoms as it brushes past them. Thus a conducting path for the electrical current connected to the electrodes (cylinder and wire) inside the tube is momentarily created and a "pulse" or gush of electricity flows between these points. It is this that is detected by the rest of the electronic apparatus comprising a counter. Such Geiger-Mueller counter tubes are commercially available.

Any teen-age boy may assemble a Geiger-Mueller counter at relatively low cost. Some of the parts used may come from old worn-out radio sets which may often be had from radio dealers almost for the asking. All other parts can be purchased at any well-stocked radio and electronic supply house.

The details of the Geiger counter about to be described were supplied by the experts of the U. S. Atomic Energy Commission. It is not complicated and may be assembled in a single evening by anyone who can handle a soldering iron. The instrument is so sensitive that it will easily detect the slight radiation from a radium-dial watch.

The following parts will be needed for the construction of this A.E.C. counter:

1. G.M. counter tube type E.P30G
2. Voltage regulator type EP30RS
3. Relay SPST normally closed
4. Step-up transformer (Thordarson Electric Co., Type 20A00)
5. 1/25-watt neon lamp
6. Three 600-volt condensers; two .01 microfarad, one .001 to .1 microfarad, one .005 microfarad

7. Two 1-watt, 1-megohm resistors
8. Toggle switch
9. Phone jack
10. Crystal headphone set
11. Neon lamp holder
12. Two flashlight cells

The complete diagram of connections for the Geiger counter is given in Fig. 32. In assembling the device all instruments are first laid out generally as illustrated and then screwed down to the wooden board. After that the connections are soldered, but we must make sure that the color code as it relates to wires is carefully followed. The color of the covering of the wires leading from the transformer is important.

If the parts of the counter have been assembled as noted, little trouble should be had in operating the device. If it is to be used for prospecting, the builder will wish to mount the assembled instruments in a wooden box provided with a handle.

Inasmuch as it would be impossible to exactly calibrate this instrument so that we would know at all times the exact intensity of the source of cosmic rays or radioactive particles at hand, we will have to be satisfied with less scientific comparisons. If we can spare a dollar, any of the chemical houses will send us a few ounces of the radioactive ore, carnotite, which can be "listened" to. (If we live in the West, many places will be found radio-

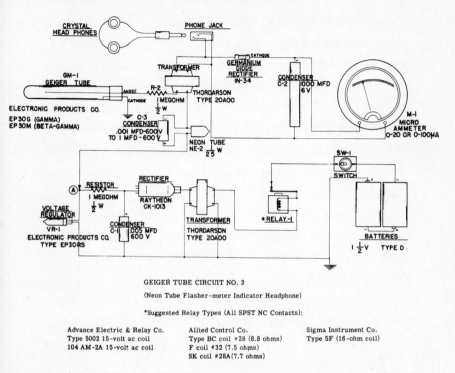

GEIGER TUBE CIRCUIT NO. 3

(Neon Tube Flasher-meter Indicator Headphone)

*Suggested Relay Types (All SPST NC Contacts):

Advance Electric & Relay Co.	Allied Control Co.	Sigma Instrument Co.
Type 5002 15-volt ac coil	Type BC coil #28 (8.8 ohms)	Type 5F (16-ohm coil)
104 AM-2A 15-volt ac coil	F coil #32 (7.5 ohms)	
	SK coil #28A (7.7 ohms)	

FIG. 32. A simple Geiger counter and the standard parts from which it may be made. Any young man who can assemble a one- or two-tube radio receiver can make this. (*Courtesy Atomic Energy Commission.*)

active enough to make the counter click happily.) After "listening" to this, we thereafter decide whether the radiation to which we are listening is below or above the standard sample.

Many very simple atomic experiments can be conducted at home with a Geiger counter but before each experiment, the user of the Geiger counter must determine the degree of what is known as background noise.

Inasmuch as cosmic rays are constantly coming into the earth and affecting a Geiger counter, such noises will always be present in varying degrees no matter where our counter may be located. If in any case, we first listen to background noise and then notice an increase in the number of clicks during an experiment we will know immediately that we are detecting increased radiation. Often we can actually count the number of clicks produced by the so-called background radiation.

One of the three types of radiation detected by the Geiger counter are gamma rays which as we stated before, are short x-rays. Such rays are produced by the radioactive substance used to make watch dials luminous. These rays travel at the speed of visible light rays (186,-000 miles per second) and they are capable of passing through certain kinds of matter, a piece of paper for example. In the case of heavier matter like lead, they are screened off or stopped.

We can easily prove this by placing a watch with a luminous dial a few inches from our Geiger counter and listen in to the number of clicks produced. We then place a piece of aluminum foil or even an aluminum pan between the watch and the counter. No reduction in the number of clicks will be noticed. However, if we replace the aluminum with a glass dish, there will be an immediate reduction in the number of clicks. Indeed the increase over the background noise will be eliminated. Not that glass alone will completely stop the gamma rays but the lead in the glass will do this.

We will also find that the electrons shot off by luminous watch dials will pass through thin sheets of paper and foil but may be stopped by our hands. Such radiation is called beta rays.

We will also note that all three radiations produced by the radioactive substances on watch dials (beta, alpha and gamma) become less and less noticeable as the watch dial is moved away from the Geiger counter. In the case of the particles (electrons or beta ray and alpha particles or helium atoms) collisions with air atoms and molecules tend to stop and scatter them beyond a few inches of travel.

If we do not wish to build our Geiger counter we may purchase one ready for use for as little as $10.00. The shopping needed to gather the parts for the counter herein described may also be avoided by the purchase of a complete assembly kit for such an instrument. These may be had at the larger supply stores handling radio and electronic equipment.

CHAPTER 10

Simple Experiments
with Radiation

THE TERM RADIATION AS USED BY PHYSICISTS has broad meaning. The light from our sun is a form of radiation as well as the heat from a furnace or a match. Indeed radio waves, light waves both visible and invisible (as infra-red, ultra-violet and x-rays) as well as heat waves are all considered as electromagnetic radiations differing only in wave length, the radio waves at the end of the electromagnetic spectrum ranging from a length of a few centimeters up to miles and the x-rays at the opposite end of the spectrum being so very short in wave length that they are capable of entering matter without being bothered a great deal about inter-atomic spaces.

Also included as radiation are the beta and alpha particles and the gamma rays shot out of radium. Then we also have neutron radiation or showers of neutrons which are probably the most dangerous of all. Thus radiation as the term is used today may be *waves* or *particles*. Cosmic rays are also considered as radiation.

No matter where we may be on the surface of the earth we cannot escape invisible radiation either in the form of cosmic rays or radioactive materials in the earth's surface. Even when we eat or drink we take in a small amount of such radioactive material and thus no human being is entirely free of internal radiation.

A list of radiations would include heat, light (visible and invisible) neutrons, electrons, protons and deuterons, etc. Some of these radiations may be stopped by a thin sheet of paper; others, like neutrons, are very difficult to stop even with walls of concrete. However, our Atomic Energy Commission has not only discovered how much radiation of different sorts can be tolerated day after day by workers and researchers in our great atomic plants but it has also perfected barriers and safeguards that guarantee freedom from hazard of any kind.

The three great factors in any sort of particle and x-ray radiation are (1) intensity, (2) distance between the source and the exposed person and (3) the nature of the barrier or protecting wall between the exposed person and the source of radiation.

There is a simple photographic experiment that will

help us in understanding the above facts. All we need is a small piece of unexposed photographic film (any kind), a radium dial from a clock or watch and a small light-tight cardboard box. If possible the glass of the watch is removed and (in the dark, of course) the dial of the watch or clock is placed face down on the sensitive side of the film. The box is then covered and set away for a few days (two to three), after which the film is developed with the results shown in Fig. 33. The brightness of the spots on the film will depend upon the length of the time of the exposure. Most by far of the light spots on the film will be caused by the x-ray (gamma) shot forth by the radioactive material in the dial numerals and hands.

To prove to our satisfaction that various materials differ in their ability to stop these radiations, we may conduct many interesting experiments with such exposures. If, for instance, we laid a thin strip of sheet lead between the face of the clock or watch and the photographic film we would discover that the lead (a dense and heavy metal) would leave a black shadow on the film proving that it effectively cut off the radiation. On the other hand, a sheet of paper would be incapable of stopping the radiation and no shadow of the paper would be found in the film. Only the slightest shadow would be left by aluminum foil and sheet copper would be almost as effective as lead. In all cases, thickness would

FIG. 33. Shadow photograph made by the author. A key and a strip of sheet copper were laid over a radium dial alarm clock after the glass was removed. A piece of photographic film was then laid on the items mentioned and the whole placed in a cardboard box with a cover for two days, after which the film was developed with the results illustrated.

be important. The brightness of the exposed portions of the film would then depend upon four factors; the intensity of the radiation, the distance and thickness of the screen or barrier and the nature of the barrier or screen. Save for neutrons, the most elusive and slippery customers among the members of the family of particle-radiation, the denser and heavier metals would be much better as screens than the lighter ones. The alpha particles are the weakest of all finding it difficult even to pass through paper.

At short distances, the gamma rays are powerful penetrators. As in the case of ordinary light waves, they diminish inversely with the square of the distance from their source. That means that the rays would lose much more than half their penetrating power if the distance between their source and a detecting device was doubled as from say 1 inch to 2 inches.

The simple electroscope described in Chapter 1 may also be used for certain radiation experiments although it is not as effective for such work as the Geiger-Mueller counter described in Chapter 9. However, for the benefit of those among us who cannot afford either to purchase or to make a counter, a few experiments with the electroscope will be described. Of course, the principal difference between the 'scope and the counter, as far as radiation experiments are concerned, is that the 'scope is much slower in its action. Whereas the counter responds to radiation (gamma or beta) instantaneously, the electroscope is pretty slow. In the case of the counter, we can quickly determine the intensity of the radiation by the number of clicks or flashes in the neon tube. In the case of the electroscope, we must measure the time or rate at which the electroscope discharges in the presence of radiation. Where low intensity radiation is present, this time may be considerable.

Of course, the first simple experiment with the electroscope is made by charging the instrument and then placing a radium-dial watch near its top and comparing the rate of discharge at various distances.

After such simple experiments, we may place sheets of paper, copper, lead, aluminum, glass, etc. between the watch dial and the electroscope to note the difference in the rate of discharge which will roughly measure the intensity of the radiation. The interposition of a sheet of lead between the dial and the electroscope should make it take just as long to discharge as during the absence of the radium-dial watch. Sheets of other materials will be found less effective in screening off the invisible rays.

If we are fortunate enough to have a homemade Geiger-Mueller counter at our disposal, many more such experiments may be made with quick results. However, with the counter we must again remember that, due to cosmic rays and in some cases to unsuspected sources of local radiation, such devices are constantly giving clicks or flashes. This radiation will vary with the various parts of the world. For instance, if we lived in a high place such as Denver, Colorado, or Mexico City, we would find that the constant cosmic radiation at those places might be from 2 to 4 times greater than it is at sea level in Boston or New York. Thus if any measurement of radiation from an artificial source is to have any scientific meaning, we must first measure the cosmic radiation and compare radiations from local sources with that radiation. This is called "determination of the background count" by nuclear physicists and we can easily understand the sense and necessity of it. If we were exploring for uranium and our counter clicked off pulses, they might be due to cosmic rays alone. However, if we had background data for the vicinity, and we came upon a section of land where the counts became much faster than the background counts, we would have more reason to believe that we were near a uranium deposit. Therefore, experiments with Geiger-Mueller counters are always preceded by a measurement of background radiation. Our radium dial or clock should be taken out of the room when such measurements are taken.

If we place a counter about 10 inches away from a radium watch dial, there should be about 11-12 flashes or clicks, per second. Placing sheets of paper or even pads of paper between the counter and the dial will produce no noticeable difference. Even one of mother's heavy aluminum frying pans or pots will offer no noticeable resistance to the passage of the rays and the particles. However, a relatively thin piece of sheet lead will quickly cut off both rays and particles and even a piece of cut glass will offer a partial screen because of the lead in the glass. Glass of this sort cuts the count from 11 per second to 3 per second. Even one's hand is sufficient to stop the high-speed electrons or beta rays. These electrons, although they move at very high speeds (up to 150,000 miles per second) are not able to penetrate great thicknesses even of very light materials.

Another simple experiment involves moving the Geiger-Mueller counter away from the radium dial at pre-determined distances and measuring the count at each point. Under these conditions the count will gradually diminish until it is reduced to the background level. The gamma rays diminish inversely with the square of the distance from the source, a fact that may very easily be proven by the simple method outlined above.

Many other simple and edifying experiments will suggest themselves to the imaginative young man.

CHAPTER 11

Atomic Merry-Go-Round

A FEW YEARS AGO A YOUNG PHYSICIST, NOW
Professor E. O. Lawrence of the University of California,
invented a machine called a cylotron. We might call it
an electromagnetic merry-go-round or an electromagnetic slingshot. We know that in one type of slingshot a
stone is carried in a leather sling mounted at the end of
a piece of rope which is swung around the head of the
operator in the manner of a lasso and at a faster and
faster rate. Finally the stone reaches such high speed and
has such great striking force that, released from the sling,
it will travel a great distance.

A simplified diagram of a cyclotron is shown in Fig. 34.
To master its method of operation we need learn only a
few simple additional facts to those already known.

We already know that electrically charged particles
like electrons and protons can be attracted or repelled

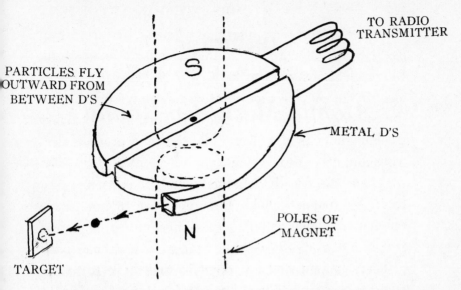

TO RADIO
TRANSMITTER

PARTICLES FLY
OUTWARD FROM
BETWEEN D'S

S

METAL D'S

TARGET

POLES OF
MAGNET

N

FIG. 34. Showing the arrangement of the D's between the powerful
magnets of a cyclotron.

as the case may be by other charged bodies. For instance, if an electron (—) passed closely enough to a positively charged metal plate, the plate would attract the electron and pull it out of its path if it did not wholly stop it and hold it. On the other hand, if a proton (+) attempted to move past the positively charged plate, it would be repelled or thrown off its normal course in a manner opposite to that of the electron.

Now it so happens that electricity or electrical charge is not the only force that can change the course of moving electrons or protons. Magnetism, either that generated by electric current passing through a wire or coils of wire (we must remember that when a wire carrying an electric current is rolled up into a coil, the magnetism, called electromagnetism because it is generated by an electric current, becomes vastly more powerful because the coil *concentrates* it) or that produced by an ordinary steel magnet can also change the course of protons, electrons and other atomic units.

When electrically charged atomic particles pass through a magnetic field (the range of attraction near a magnet or an electromagnet) the effect of the magnetism is that of causing the particles to *move in a circular path*.

There is another basic point we will have to understand before we can know how the cyclotron works. We again refer to the fact that a charged atomic particle is always drawn toward or repelled by a charged body. We must know that the speed with which such particles are drawn to such bodies will depend upon the power or intensity of the charge upon the plate. If this electric charge is very high (such charges are always measured in the terms of volts and any voltage between say 5000 and 100,000 volts might be called high) the speed with which the atomic particles are drawn toward the charged plate will be great. Under certain conditions which vary with the type of equipment used, electric charges may be used greatly to increase the speed of such atomic particles. For instance, the speed of electrons may be increased to well over 100,000 miles per *second*.

When the speed of particles heavier than electrons are greatly accelerated (speeded up) these particles may then be used as bullets with which to bombard atoms and thereby to bring about certain changes within them. Electrons could not be used for this work because, we might say, they are the babies of the family of atomic particles. They are too light and too small for such business, being only 1/1840th of the weight of an atom of hydrogen which we recall has only a single proton in its nucleus with a single electron revolving around it. Thus do we see that the electron forms very little of the mass or weight of any atom. It is the protons and the neutrons that count most.

The cyclotron (see Fig. 35) is a huge, heavy device designed to speed up atomic particles so that such particles may be used to bombard whole atoms. The simplified parts of a cyclotron, minus all of its complicated accessories, are shown. Here we will notice a large metal chamber in the shape of a split pillbox, each half insulated from the other. A large radio transmitter is connected to these two semicircular sections of metal. Really the two sections of metal take the place of a radio transmitter antenna or aerial. In place of the electrical energy coming from the radio transmitter being broadcast into space in the form of electric or radio waves, it is instead carried to these sections of metal usually referred to as D's because of their shape. In short, what is known as the

Fig. 35. A small cyclotron in the physics building at the University of Rochester.

output current of the radio transmitter is connected to these D's.

We have two classes of electric current; one called *direct* which constantly flows in a single direction and one called *alternating* which constantly changes its direction, going first in one direction and then stopping abruptly and going in the opposite direction. Alternating current can be made to change its direction (cycles) from a few times each second to many millions of times per second.

Now all electric currents flow from positive to negative. In the case of a dry cell which always supplies direct current, the cell has a positive pole and a negative one, the current flowing from the positive to the negative without variation.

In the case of a radio transmitter what is known as a high-frequency (high rate of changing its direction) current is produced. This rate of change may vary from a few thousand changes per second to many millions depending upon how the electrical circuits and parts of the radio transmitter are designed. Thus when the output current of such a transmitter is connected to the D's of a cyclotron, the D's will change their electrical charge each time a reversal of current takes place. For an extremely small fraction of a second, a D will be charged negatively. Then when a rapid reversal of the current takes place, the D will become positively charged, the process continuing as long as the current flows. At the same time the D's are in a powerful magnetic field which forces the particles to take a circular course.

Now let us see what might happen to, say a proton (+) particle if it was released directly in the center of the circle made up by the two D's. At the instant of release, the proton, being positive, would be attracted to the D which at that instant was negative inasmuch as opposite charges of electricity attract each other. This attraction between the negative D and the positive proton would last but the tiniest fraction of a second, however. Soon the charged particle in the D would find itself in a very hostile place which would repel it and tend to kick it out we might say.

In the meantime the other D would have become negative and would attract the bewildered proton. Instantly the proton would rush out of the hostile space and move at very high speed over to the negative D. This action takes place at a very high speed but not too high for the proton to respond because it is a very small and light particle perfectly able to keep pace with the changing electrical charges.

If the magnetism was not present, the proton would spend its time merely rushing back and forth in a straight line between the D's. We were told previously, however, that when moving charged particles are placed in a magnetic field that *they tend to move in a circle, the curvature of the circle depending upon the power of the magnetic field.* Thus this proton in place of just shuttling back and forth between the D's in a perfectly straight line, would move in a circle between the D's. Nor would this circle be one of constant diameter. The effect of the electrical attraction between the D's is that of speeding up the proton. The faster the proton moves the less effect the magnetic field will have on it and the larger the circle described by it will be.

What really happens then is that the proton keeps spiraling outward going faster and faster at each swing around until finally (and all of this in an extremely small fraction of second) it has reached the outer limits of the wall of the hollow D's moving at maximum speed which may amount to many thousands of miles per second. This speed is so great that should this rapidly moving atomic bullet be flung at an atom and strike it squarely the atom would suffer certain damage and rearrangement by bombardment. The question is: How are we going to snatch the proton from this very busy merry-go-round?

This is done (see Fig. 34 again) very simply and by means of what is known as a deflector plate which itself carries a very high and powerful electric charge. Inasmuch as our particle, the proton, carries a positive charge, the charge on the deflector plate must be negative.

As the high-speed proton rushes past the deflector plate, it will not be drawn directly to it but it will be drawn slightly out of the curved or circular path that it has been following, enough so that it will be caused to shoot out of an opening placed on the edge of one of the D's. Directly beyond this opening is a small compartment in which the chemical or element (a very small amount) is placed to be bombarded. Thus does the high-speed proton go crashing into this substance. Of course, in place of a single proton, countless millions of high-speed protons are created in actual operation and only a few of them so produced strike their atom targets within the substance under bombardment. Most of them miss by a wide margin.

If in place of the bombardment chamber, a small metal window is used, the high-speed protons easily crash through this and are permitted to escape into the outside atmosphere leaving a weird blue trail after them for a distance of a foot or more depending upon the power of the cyclotron that produced them. Such beams are deadly. If we exposed ourselves to them directly for a few seconds death would not be long in following.

When a cyclotron is in operation as much air as possible in the chamber occupied by the D's must be pumped out. Otherwise the fast-moving protons would be slowed down by bumping along between the atoms and the molecules of the gases that go to make up the atmosphere. It is for this reason that the high-speed protons leaving the cyclotron by means of the window are quickly brought to a walk. The bluish color produced by the stream of protons is caused by the proton colliding with the atoms of the air gases.

Although a few other atomic particles can be made to reach high speed in the cyclotron and to be thereby used for bombardment purposes, it will be clear to us that the neutron cannot be so used. Introduced between the D's of a cyclotron, the neutron being neither electrically positive or negative, would be unaffected by the changing charges on the D's. It might wander slowly about. However, even when wandering slowly, the neutron is a more effective bombardment particle than are high-speed protons because while the proton and other atomic bombardment particles must be pumped up to great speeds before they can crash into the nuclei of atoms, the neutron can wander into atom cores slowly because it has no hostility to meet it. After having so wandered into the nuclei of some very heavy atoms such as uranium it can cause much mischief, more indeed than any other particle regardless of its speed. The neutron is indeed the sub-atomic bomb, the stealthy intruder which, once inside an atom of uranium, so disarranges the natural order of things that the uranium atom cannot endure the strain and blows up. Therein lies the story of the atom bomb.

Cyclotrons and other super-electronic devices that speed up electrically charged atomic particles have produced much information by the bombardment of matter.

By the use of the cyclotron, the physicist has changed the basic nature of many elements; actually transmuted them. It is quite true that only microscopic amounts have been changed into other elements but that does not deny that actual transmutation has taken place.

CHAPTER 12

How the Atomic
Bomb Works

BACK IN CHAPTER 5, WE LEARNED THAT WHEN atoms are put together as in the case of two atoms of hydrogen forming one atom of the gas helium, there can be a release of energy resulting from the conversion of a small amount of mass. We also learned that when atoms fly apart either naturally as in the case of radium or by methods that have been perfected by our nuclear physicists, a certain small percentage of mass is also converted into energy. In the case of the atomic bomb, the latter process is involved. Atoms are dispersed, broken into smaller units. If the mass or weights of the smaller units resulting from the explosion were gathered up and weighed, the total weight or mass of these units would be slightly less than the mass or weight of the atom that blew up. The difference would be that portion of the atom that disappeared as energy. Some of the released energy would take the form of intense invisible light or x-rays (light is a form of energy) and heat which as we all know is also a wave form of energy.

Some idea of the tremendous heat (principally) liberated by an atomic explosion may be had when it is known that a level teaspoonful of the isotope of uranium (235) used in the atomic bomb is equal to 200,000 gallons of gasolene or 300,000 pounds of coal. This means that we must multiply the energy produced by coal by 5,000,000 and that produced by gasolene by 3,000,000. Here, however, we are not talking about the total energy in this small amount of the uranium isotope but only the small fraction of energy that is released as a result of the splitting of the atom. The nuclear energy released by the *total* conversion of a single gram of matter into energy would be sufficient to raise 3000 locomotives to a height of 25 miles. When matter is completely converted into energy, it is 18,000,000,000 times more powerful than the ordinary combustion or burning of coal.

During the year 1940 atomic or nuclear physicists began shooting neutrons into the blackish-gray, heavy metal uranium known to be mildly radioactive on its own account.

When neutron slugs entered ordinary uranium, the physicists noticed that tremendous puffs of energy were released. Instruments showed that these puffs of energy although small, were for their size and all things considered, the most powerful ever set forth.

The uranium into which the lazy neutron slugs were shot behaved something like a package of partially defective firecrackers. There would be very irregular explosions so long as the neutrons kept coming on but the explosions ceased immediately the neutron flow ceased. The physicists were pretty sure that atoms inside the uranium were blowing up but, once ignited, why didn't they all go? The answer to that question proved to be the answer to the atomic bomb.

What at first bothered and mystified these early experimenters with their at first fitful and capricious atomic explosions was the fact that after they took place, a small amount of the element barium was found to be present although it was not there when the bombardment of uranium with neutrons was begun. Where did it come from and how did it get there? Was it one of the smaller pieces broken off an atom of uranium after the wily neutron had slipped into the nucleus?

Uranium has an atomic weight of 92 whereas barium has a weight of 56. If a fragment of the split-up atom of uranium turned out to be barium, what happened to the piece of the atom that was left? When the atomic weight of the metal barium (56) is subtracted from the atomic weight of uranium (92) the result is 36. Therefore if a single fragment was left after a piece equal to the atomic weight of the barium atom was broken off this piece should have a weight of 36. Was there a known atom with such a weight? Yes, there was and it was the rare atmospheric gas, krypton. Could it be that the invading neutrons split the atom of uranium into barium and krypton?

The nuclear physicists calculated that the atomic energy released by such a split would amount exactly to the release of energy that was accurately measured when the neutrons caused the irregular explosions.

Uranium was known to exist in its natural state as a combination of isotopes, U234, U235 and (mostly) U238. U235 is present only as 1 part in 140. Could it be that the isotope U235 was especially sensitive to neutron bombardment and that the other isotopes of uranium present, U234 and U238, were not and that these isotopes functioned as the wet sawdust in the package of atomic firecrackers? If the researchers had some pure U235, they would soon answer that question. Finally, a few trillionths of a gram of pure U235 was supplied and exposed to neutron bombardment. That was the answer. A terrific although microscopic explosion took place, the first true atomic bomb although its substance could easily have been placed on the head of a pin.

The next problem that remained for the would-be makers of an atomic bomb was the then almost hopeless task of finding a commercial process for separating the isotope U235 from its tight association (natural) with U238 and U234.

Finally through the cooperation of the large manufacturers of the U.S.A., U235 was produced in quantities large enough for use in atomic bombs. While there are other methods of producing atomic explosions, their introduction would at this time serve only to confuse us. After all the general principles of all such explosions are the same and if we can understand such explosions as produced by U235, we will have prepared ourselves to continue our studies in other and more advanced books if we so desire.

Turning to the crude diagram in Fig. 36 will help us to master the essentials of the U235 bomb. Here for purposes of simplicity we start out with a single atom of U235 in the immediate presence of a few other U235 atoms. A single atom of U235 is struck with a single neutron which quickly slides into the nucleus of this atom and so upsets the balance of things there that it succeeds in breaking this atom up into the atoms of krypton and barium. When this violent eruption takes place, other neutrons from the struck atoms themselves are set free and these enter the nuclei of adjacent U235 atom causing the same thing to happen; these atoms in turn split and produce more neutrons, etc. Finally in a small fraction of a millionth of a second, tremendous showers of neutrons pervade the U235 atom and split

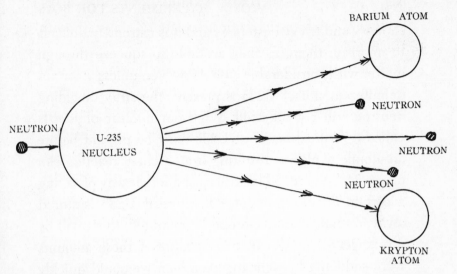

FIG. 36.   How the explosion of one atom and the release of neutrons is communicated to adjacent atoms on an ever-increasing scale. After the U235 atom explodes it leaves free neutrons and the atoms of barium and krypton.

them asunder with tremendous release of atomic energy. This is the process of fission on a mass scale which has become known as the chain reaction. It amounts to the quick spreading of fission or splitting brought about by a single sub-atomic bullet, the neutron. However, this is not the end of our story.

For reasons that need not be discussed here, it is not enough merely that a stray neutron invade an atom of U235 to set up an explosion that cannot be stopped. It is also very fortunate that this is true. Otherwise we could not produce a stockpile of U235. Neutrons are pretty slippery and tricky customers and it is extremely difficult to imprison them, as they are able to squeeze through matter with considerable ease. However, unless a certain definite amount of U235 is present, the stray, invading neutron will not set it off. What our nuclear physicists called a "critical mass" of U235 must be present before an atomic explosion resulting from a chain reaction can take place. A "critical mass" is just another way of saying a certain definite amount. Therefore if U235 is stored away in small amounts, properly separated, there will be no danger. If, however, two or more of these amounts were suddenly brought together then we could quickly have an atomic explosion.

Almost without our knowing it, we have stated the principle used in exploding atomic bombs. It is assumed that 3 non-critical masses of U235 (say 5 pounds each) are separated by a safe distance within an atomic bomb. At the moment of explosion, a mechanical mechanism within the bomb operates to bring these non-critical masses together to form a critical mass. Explosion results. That is the way the first bombs operated although it is now believed that research has provided methods that will cause the explosions of masses of U235 that were once considered to be non-critical.

CHAPTER 13

The Atomic Pile

WE HAVE SEEN THAT, IN THE CASE OF THE atomic bomb, neutrons can be released wildly and to such a degree that U235 or plutonium can be made to break up with tremendous violence. In such cases millions of horsepower of force can be released in a small fraction of a second. If this process could be so controlled that such a release of energy could be slowed down or stretched out over a long period of time, the thermo or heat energy set free could be used in a practical manner. This would be something like exploding a bunch of firecrackers; we can set them all off at one time or set them off one at a time.

This business of slowing down the release of atomic energy would be impossible were it not for the fact that the motion of neutrons can be controlled. Fortunately for the future of atomic energy there are certain substances such as ordinary graphite (a form of carbon used in lead pencils) or the metal cadmium that, when used as screens, are capable of slowing down or stopping neutrons. Thus when relatively large and otherwise explosive (critical) amounts of U235 or plutonium are arranged in a certain manner, the process of fission can be controlled so as to go just so far and no further; far enough to produce useful quantities of atomic materials and of heat but not far enough to produce a quick explosion. This is something like a steam boiler with a safety valve vs. one without a safety valve. Pieces of carbon and cadmium or tanks of heavy water can function as safety valves for "atomic boilers" and such "boilers" are called atomic piles. Here we have the *gradual* release of energy. In such piles, chain reactions take place but they are kept within bounds.

In such piles the rods of cadmium and carbon bricks that are used are called moderators; really speed reducers for neutrons. A slow neutron is more easily swerved from a straight line than a fast one and slow neutrons, strangely enough, produce more fission than do fast ones.

The energy released by an atomic pile can also be controlled by diluting the amount of U235 present with U238 or thorium which is something like adding kerosene to gasolene which would make the latter much less explosive. Fission control in an ideal atomic pile amounts to the maintenance of an even rate at a pre-determined level; neither too low to be useless or too high to be explosive.

As used today, the atomic pile is a vastly complicated mechanism with a large degree of autimic control and associated with many electronic and mechanical devices. The best that we can hope to do here is to reduce such a mechanism to its simplest basic principle and thereby gain such a toe hold that, should we wish to continue our study elsewhere, we will have at least mastered the ABC's of the subject.

The successful construction of an atomic pile was not, however, merely a matter of moderators within the pile to control the movement and speed of neutrons. Neutron radiation is the most dangerous to which humans can be exposed. Hence, such piles had to be sealed off with thick neutron and x-ray barriers to protect the men who worked around them.

Returning to the subject of fission vs. slow and fast neutrons let us put it this way. With a given amount of ordinary uranium (we must remember that uranium as it comes from nature is a mixture of U235, U238 and U234) the movement of neutrons constantly being discharged from the U235 is so fast that most of them by far escape without producing fission. In short, nothing much happens. However, if we arrange this uranium within a pile of graphite blocks so that all of these released neutrons will be slowed down and thereby made more effective in producing fission, fission can be tremendously accelerated. There will then be much more prospect of released neutrons entering the nucleus of other U235 atoms which in turn release still more neutrons to repeat the action. The chain effect is thereby greatly increased by the simple trick of a reduction in neutron speed.

The first simple pile, called a lattice (see Fig. 37), was set up in 1941 at Columbia University. It amounted to

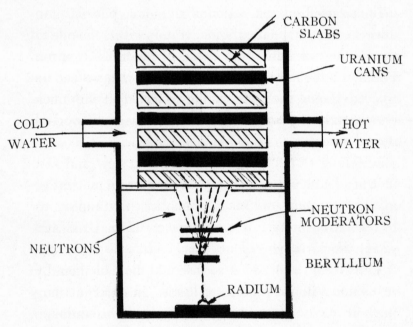

FIG. 37. A simple atomic pile wherein neutron release is initiated by radium bombardment of the metal beryllium.

a pile of graphite bricks $8 \times 8 \times 8$ feet throughout which there was distributed 7 tons of purified uranium. Beneath this pile there was placed a small mixture of radium and beryllium which generated still another source (the U235 within the uranium being one) of neutrons which neutrons found their way into the pile above. Here the scientists sought information on the "multiplication factor" or the rate of growth of the chain reaction principle. This first fission took place at an increased rate but still far from the point where it would maintain itself automatically or get out of control to produce a concentrated explosion. It only greatly increased the number ot individual "explosions" of U235 atoms. Fermi, the brilliant nuclear physicist who worked on this, the first of the piles, estimated that this multiplication factor could be greatly increased by increasing the size of the pile, the amount and the purity of its components.

When finally a much larger pile was set up in Chicago, a pile that wholly confirmed Fermi's idea that the answer to the problem lay in size and purity of materials, the scientists who engineered the larger pile, took the precaution of certain safety measures should the fission tend to rush on to a point of quick explosion. This precautionary measure took the form of rods of the metal cadmium which not only slows neutrons down but is capable of stopping many of them by locking them in absorption;

a neutron sponge, we might call it. When the operation of the pile was started, these rods, carefully located in respect to the active neutron paths within the pile, were left where they could either be pushed into or pulled out of the pile to control the "neutron flux" or density.

If it was observed that the pile began building up fission at too rapid a rate, the process could be stopped by merely pushing the rods into the pile.

As the controls of this atomic pile were gradually released, fission also gradually increased as anticipated. At each increase in the flow of neutrons, the instruments and the audible clickings of the Geiger-Mueller counters present indicated a much higher level of fission. Eventually, however, this would tend to die out. At this point, neutron flow was again increased. The scientists present, and especially Dr. Fermi, were sure that at some point along the line the intensity of the neutron flow would be great enough so that the fission would continue automatically at a very high level. The approximate level was known but the approach had to be cautious. After all, these men were dealing with lethal substances; a new and terrible form of explosive force. A miscalculation might have meant the end of all of them as well as that of the immediate neighborhood.

After a number of hours of operation and of gradual increase in the flow of neutrons, a point was finally reached where the action, no longer tapered off. The needles of the indicating instruments remained at a certain point and the clatter of the audible Geiger-Mueller counters remained at a very high level; a loud buzzing sound. A point had been reached where the action of fission *maintained itself automatically.*

Since those days we have not only greatly improved atomic piles but we have a much wider application of such things; applications that have nothing to do with atomic bombs; applications directed at the saving of human life rather than at its wholesale destruction. It is in these "atomic cooking ovens" that the radioactive isotopes are created that now offer such promise to medical and industrial research. The atoms of common materials such as carbon, iodine or phosphorus, once exposed to the heavy neutron "storms" within the atomic pile themselves become radioactive isotopes.

From a small 8-foot square cube, atomic piles have grown to such magnitude that elevators are necessary for the men who watch over them. Each pile is encased in a protective shield of concrete 5 feet thick. Within such confines there would be space enough for living quarters for a family of six. Whereas the first little pile used at Columbia University weighed only a few tons, the big piles of today weigh thousands of tons. Each pile is able to maintain the fission process continuously, its intensity always within the range of precise control.

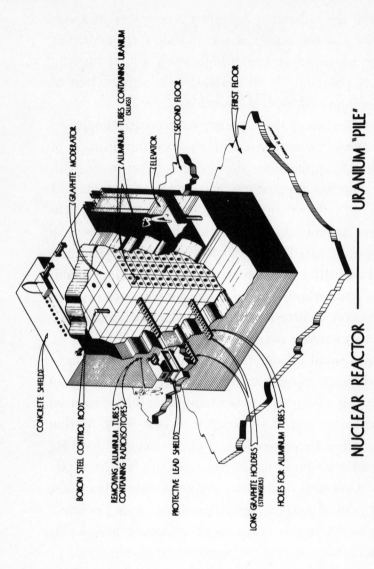

NUCLEAR REACTOR — URANIUM "PILE"

Labels on figure:
CONCRETE SHIELD
BORON STEEL CONTROL ROD
REMOVING ALUMINUM TUBES CONTAINING RADIOISOTOPES
PROTECTIVE LEAD SHIELD
LONG GRAPHITE HOLDERS (STRINGERS)
HOLES FOR ALUMINUM TUBES
GRAPHITE MODERATOR
ALUMINUM TUBES CONTAINING URANIUM (SLUGS)
ELEVATOR
SECOND FLOOR
FIRST FLOOR

FIG. 38. A great nuclear reactor or uranium pile of the type now in use. It is so large that its attendants have to use electric elevators to service it. (Courtesy Atomic Energy Commission.)

CHAPTER 14

Atomic Power

WE HAVE SEEN THAT THE BULK OF THE energy released by atomic explosions, either rapid as in the case of the bomb or slow and orderly as in the case of the atomic pile, is in the form of heat. This is the same sort of heat that toasts our toes before the hearth or brews the morning coffee.

Atomic piles generate great volumes of heat the amount depending upon their size and the intensity of the fission going on within them. In the case of one of our great atomic plants, a whole river (the Columbia) is used to carry away the heat generated; heat that, under proper conditions, might be employed usefully. Every atomic pile, no matter how it is designed, must be cooled. Otherwise the heat it generated would build up to a point where great damage would be done. In a certain new type of atomic pile, molten bismuth metal will be circulated through it by special pipes and made to flow out again where it will be cooled and returned to the job. By keeping a cool liquid flowing through atomic piles in this way, they can be made into continuous carriers of heat.

Therein lies the germ of using atomic power for practical purposes. We can easily see how it might be possible to heat and vaporize water into steam within a special atomic pile and to carry this steam either to an engine or a turbine which in turn would be connected to an electric generator. That approach amounts to our first hope of converting atomic energy into useful power. The present experiments now being made are along these lines.

This, of course, is a far cry from the atomic powered automobile, airplane, locomotive or rocket. Always in this atomic energy and power business, we must think of the safety of the people who will operate such plants.

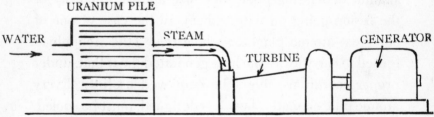

FIG. 39.   One method of converting atomic energy into a usable form is to permit a uranium pile to serve in the place of a steam boiler, the heat being applied to water to make steam.

Heavy barriers must be set up between the operators and the plant itself if radiation is not to bring slow or even quick death. No automobile, airplane or even locomotive could carry such equipment today although submarines and battleships can if we are to believe our atomic scientists. Some day perhaps, we shall so improve our mastery over the movements of neutrons and over the dangerous radiation set up by fission, that small, lightweight atomic power plants can be made for use in automobiles and planes. If it can be done at all, years of research may be required. On the other hand, of course, we can never discount or completely rule out the possibility of a quickly made discovery that will make such a power plant commercially practical almost overnight. Such is the nature of the fast-moving world in which we live.

CHAPTER 15

The H-Bomb

BACK IN CHAPTER 5, WE HAD SOMETHING TO
say about the union of 2 atoms of hydrogen to form 1
atom of the gas helium. We also learned that the weight
of 1 atom of helium was *less* than the sum of 2 atoms of
hydrogen and that when such a union takes place, this
small amount of mass is converted into energy. It is this
combination of 2 atoms of hydrogen to form 1 of helium
that is supposed to be taking place on the sun and to
supply that body with the heat that makes of it the huge
solar furnace without which life on this planet would be
impossible. We forgot to mention, however, that the
energy set free by this combination is calculated to be
1000 times greater than that released by the now-familiar
explosion of the atomic bomb. The Atomic Energy Commission is already at work setting up great plants for the

production of ingredients of this fearsome new agent of destruction.

We used the term "fission" in connection with the atomic explosion. This refers to the splitting apart of atoms. With the hydrogen bomb, based as it is on the *union* of atoms we must use the word "fusion" which means welding together.

While atomic energy as we know of it in connection with the atomic bomb offers untold promise as a peace-time aid to our country and to the world at large, the hydrogen bomb offers nothing but an uncontrollable release of energy for purely military purposes. Unlike ordinary atomic reactions that can be tamed and slowed down in such a way as to make a slow, continuous flow of useful energy available for power purposes and industry, the hydrogen reaction cannot be so controlled once it is started.

The A-bomb is set off when two or more small masses of fissionable material suddenly come into proximity or close range to form what the physicists call a critical mass. No external energy whatever is applied and the resulting explosion releases tremendous amounts of energy, much of it thermal or heat energy.

In the case of a firecracker, we must apply heat to the powder charge if we are to set off an explosion purely chemical in nature. This is done with a fuse. The hydrogen bomb also requires a fuse but something more powerful than a mere match. Here we must have heat measured in millions of degrees. There is only one thing that can supply the amount of heat necessary and that is the A-bomb. Therefore the hydrogen bomb must be a combination of bombs, an A-bomb within the hydrogen bomb which acts as the "fuse" and which must go off first to supply the heat necessary to stimulate the hydrogen bomb explosion.

At present we know only that the hydrogen bomb will involve some sort of hydrogen reaction. The rest is speculation for reasons of security. Aside from the mere combination of ordinary hydrogen atoms to form helium atoms as has been previously described there are other reactions involving heavy (double-weight) hydrogen and tritium or triple-weight hydrogen. Ordinary hydrogen such as we breathe from the air is now called protium and heavy hydrogen is called deuterium.

Speculation shows that a number of combinations are possible to produce H-bomb explosions. For one, the meeting of a proton and tritium might be used. Then there is a possibility of bringing tritium and deuterium together in the presence of high heat to create an explosion. Still another possibility is the meeting of lithium and deterium or lithium and protons.

CHAPTER 16

Prospecting for Uranium

SUCH A BOOK AS THIS MIGHT NOT BE COM-
plete unless some mention of prospecting for uranium
was made. All of the technical know-how imaginable
will be of no use unless the U.S.A. has ample supplies
of uranium, the basic material making possible not only
the A-bomb and power-producing atomic piles but the
H-bomb as well. At the present time the uranium supply
is not known to be inexhaustible. We do not yet know
where the end is precisely but we do know that whatever
it is in all probability it is not enough. Our country must
ever be on the alert to discover new deposits where concentration will be sufficient to warrant the labor and cost
of recovery. The hunt is on. A new type of Forty-niner
is searching the surface of the earth for a substance still
more precious than gold, more useful than gold and far
more important to the future of the United States.

Further to stimulate active interest in this search for uranium, our Atomic Energy Commission is offering not only assistance but rewards. Those who discover deposits beyond a specified range of concentration capable of producing a certain definite tonnage will receive a bonus of $10,000 and even this may amount to but a small percentage of the wealth that will come to the prospectors who spot the deposit.

Uranium and other radioactive materials are distributed over the surface of the earth but not evenly so. Some spots are richer than others. On the whole this heavy, grayish metal makes up only 1/10000th of the earth's crust. In some discovered and in some still undiscovered spots the concentration greatly exceeds this figure. Therein, by the nature of things in this modern atomic world, lies the future of the United States; its future as a military power, its future as an industrial giant and its future in social progress with plenty for all.

Already the new prospectors, young and old, are out combing the surface of the U.S.A. with their Geiger-Mueller counters. Where the states of Utah, Colorado, Arizona and New Mexico converge, the new prospectors are fanning out over the hills and the plateaus. Some ore is also known to be present in Nevada, Wyoming, Montana and Michigan. These great areas are known to contain uranium oxide deposits (U_3O_4) of varying amounts, some too low to bother with, some rich enough to work and perhaps some, as yet undiscovered, that will make rich men out of those who find them. Already little mines privately discovered and privately operated have been opened in this region and always there is the Atomic Energy Commission willing and eager not only to offer assistance and guidance but to purchase at a good figure every precious ton of acceptable ore brought to the surface. Unlike the bearded prospectors of old, the newcomers are young men who search and dig and sample or who operate their own deposits always with the chance of striking an unsuspected bonanza.

On the whole the mining operations are of a simple kind usually near the surface and located high enough on the ranges to avoid the need for water pumping equipment. Nor do these young miners need to invest in heavy and expensive drilling or ore handling equipment. Some enterprising, hard-working young men depend upon nothing more complicated or costly than pickaxes, shovels and wheelbarrows. Such is the need for uranium that there is room both for the small operator and the large one. A few deposits have been found so near the surface that what is known as open-pit mining is possible.

For young men not afraid to soil their hands or develop their muscles, the pay for working even a moderately rich deposit can be good and the market always steady and depression proof. Uncle Sam's need and pocketbook guarantees that. Fair ore brings over $10.00 per ton while top ore may bring as high as $66.00 per ton. The work may be hard but it has the smell of the earth in it and the romance of the pioneer. Always there is the prospect of the "big strike" and the big money.